SADLIER

VOCABULARY WORKSHOP

C Common Core Enriched Edition

Level G

Jerome Shostak

Senior Series Consultant

Vicki A. Jacobs, Ed.D.
Associate Director, Teacher Education Program
Lecturer on Education
Harvard Graduate School of Education
Cambridge, Massachusetts

Series Consultants

Louis P. De Angelo, Ed.D.
Associate Superintendent
Diocese of Wilmington
Wilmington, Delaware

John Heath, Ph.D.
Professor of Classics
Santa Clara University
Santa Clara, California

Sarah Ressler Wright, NBCT
English Department Chair
Rutherford B. Hayes High School
Delaware City Schools, Ohio

Carolyn E. Waters, JD, Ed.S.
ELA/Literacy 6–12 Supervisor
Cobb County School District
Marietta, Georgia

Sadlier

Reviewers

The publisher wishes to thank for their comments and suggestions the following teachers and administrators, who read portions of the series prior to publication.

Cover: Concept/Art and Design: MK Advertising and William H. Sadlier, Inc.; Cover pencil: Shutterstock/VikaSuh.
Photo Credits: Interior: akg-images: 65, 21; IAM/World History Archive: 126 *bottom*; National Maritime Museum: 126 *bottom right*, 127. Alamy/Amoret Tanner: 55; Classic Image: 184 *top*; Corbis: 108 *inset*; Courtesy: CSU Archives/Everett Collection: 113; Danita Delimont/Claudia Adams: 146 *bottom right*; David Levenson: 169; Dmitry Rukhlenko-Travel Photos: 147 *bottom right*; Felix Stensson: 75; Judith Collins: 131; Karen Debler: 41; Keystone Pictures USA: 89 *top right*; Lebrecht Music and Arts Photo Library: 145; North Wind Picture Archives: 189; Pictorial Press Ltd: 89 *top left*, 193; The Print Collector: 117. AP Images/Louis Lanzano: 71. Art Resource, NY/2009 Museum Associates/LACMA: 147 *bottom left*; DeA Picture Library: 146 *bottom left*; The Art Archive/Society of the Friends of Music Vienna/Collection Dagli Orti: 37; The Kobal Collection/Working Title: 173; The Metropolitan Museum of Art: 61; Werner Forman: 27. Blend/LatinStock Collection: 108 *bottom left*. Corbis: 33 *top center*, 99 *bottom center*; Ali Hashisho/X01161/Reuters: 51 *inset*; Bettmann: 141; Classic Stock/H. Armstrong Roberts: 151; David J. & Janice L. Frent Collection: 32, 33 *top left*; J.S. Johnston: 22; Jack Kurtz/ZUMA Press: 70; Michael Ochs Archives: 88; Mike Segar/Reuters: 23 *top right*; Richard Berenholtz: 50 *background*; Science Faction/Michael Rosenfeld: 174 *bottom left*; Sheng Hong/Xinhua Press: 50 *inset*; Underwood & Underwood: 164; Xinhua Press/Xinhua/Yuri Gripas: 98 *bottom left*. Digitalvision: 108 *background*. Estate of Roy Lichtenstein/Private Collection: 60. Everett Collection: 31, 59, 69; Almi Pictures: 97; Cinecom International: 135; Focus features: 107. Georgia Institute of Technology, College of Computing: 175 *bottom left*. Getty Images/AFP/Don Emmert: 175 *top left*; Fotosearch/Stringer: 33; New York Daily News/Joe Petrella: 165 *bottom left*; Time & Life Pictures: 79, 137 *bottom*; Topical Press Agency/Stringer: 103. The Granger Collection, NYC: 13 *center*, 155, 183. Lebrecht Authors: 93. Library of Congress Prints & Photographs Division, Washington, DC: 184 *bottom*. Mary Evans Picture Library: 137 *bottom*. NASA: 137 *top*. National Portrait Gallery/Smithsonian Institution: 99 *bottom left*. National Portrait Gallery, London: 185 *top*. Photo Researchers, Inc./Science Source: 179. The New York Public Library, Astor, Lenox and Tilden Foundations Picture Collection: 23 *top insets*. Photodisc: 98, 99 *frame*, 126 *bottom right*, 127; Punchstock: 98. Shutterstock: Angelina Dimitrova: 88 *background*; ARENA Creative: 60 *background*; argus: 174; boumen&japet: 13 *frame*; Daboost: 108 *center*; Johann Helgason: 33 *top border*; Michaela Stejskalova: 12 *background*; Myotis: 50 *frame*, 51 *frame*; Neo Edmund: 146; Taiga: 70; Thomas Bethge: 164; VikaSuh: 1. US Patent Office: 165 *bottom right*. WHS: 23 *top*. Wikipedia Commons: 17.

Illustration Credits: Tim Haggerty: 46, 84, 122, 160, 198.

For additional online resources, go to vocabularyworkshop.com **and enter the Student Access Code: VW12SGCA47NP**

C ENRICHED EDITION: New Features

For more than five decades, VOCABULARY WORKSHOP has proven to be a highly successful tool for guiding systematic vocabulary growth and developing vocabulary skills. It has also been shown to help students prepare for standardized tests.

New in this edition are the **Reading Passages, Writing, Vocabulary in Context,** and **Word Study** activities. Nonfiction, high-interest passages use 15 or more of the Unit vocabulary words in context. Two writing prompts require a response to the reading and provide practice in writing for standardized tests. New Vocabulary in Context activities present words from the Unit as they are used in classic works of literature. After every three units, Word Study activities, developed in conjunction with Common Core State Standards requirements, provide practice with idioms, adages, and proverbs, as well as denotation and connotation and classical roots.

Look for the new **QR** (Quick Response) codes on the **Reading Passage** and **Vocabulary in Context** pages. The code can be read with a smartphone camera. To read the QR code, download any free QR code application to a smartphone. Snap the code with a smartphone camera to go directly to iWords for the Unit or an interactive quiz. With iWords you can listen to one word at a time or download all of the words in a Unit to listen to them at your convenience.

The new structure of VOCABULARY WORKSHOP is made up of 15 Units. Each Unit consists of the following sections: a **Reading Passage, Definitions, Choosing the Right Word, Synonyms and Antonyms, Completing the Sentence, Writing,** and **Vocabulary in Context**. Together, these exercises provide multiple and varied exposures to the taught words—an approach consistent with and supportive of research-based findings in vocabulary instruction.

Five **Reviews** cover Vocabulary for Comprehension and Two-Word Completions. Vocabulary for Comprehension is modeled on the reading sections of standardized tests, and as in those tests, it presents reading comprehension questions, including specific vocabulary-related ones, that are based on a reading passage.

A **Final Mastery Test** assesses a selection of words from the year with activities on Synonyms, Antonyms, Analogies, Two-Word Completions, Supplying Words in Context, Word Associations, and Choosing the Right Meaning.

In each level of VOCABULARY WORKSHOP, 300 key words are taught. The words have been selected according to the following criteria: currency and general usefulness; frequency of appearance on recognized vocabulary lists; applicability to, and appearance on, standardized tests; and current grade-level research.

ONLINE COMPONENTS
vocabularyworkshop.com

At **vocabularyworkshop.com** you will find iWords, an audio program that provides pronunciations, definitions, and examples of usage for all of the key words presented in this level of VOCABULARY WORKSHOP. You can listen to one word at a time or, if you wish, download to an MP3 player all of the words of any given Unit. You will then be able to listen to the audio program for that Unit at your convenience.

At **vocabularyworkshop.com** you will also find **interactive vocabulary quizzes, flashcards, games and puzzles** that will help reinforce and enrich your understanding of the key words in this level of VOCABULARY WORKSHOP.

CONTENTS

iWords Audio Program available at **vocabularyworkshop.com**.

VOCABULARY STRATEGY: Using Context

The **context** of a word is the printed text of which that word is part. By studying the word's context, we may find **clues** to its meaning. We might find a clue in the immediate or adjoining sentence or phrase in which the word appears; in the topic or subject matter of the passage; or in the physical features—such as photographs, illustrations, charts, graphs, captions and headings—of a page itself.

The **Vocabulary in Context**, **Vocabulary for Comprehension**, and **Choosing the Right Meaning** exercises that appear in the Units, the Reviews, and Final Mastery Test provide practice in using context to decode unfamiliar words.

Three types of context clues appear in the exercises in this book.

A **restatement clue** consists of a *synonym* for or a *definition* of the missing word. For example:

I peered through the gloomy hall and made out an equally _____ room at the end of it.

a. fragrant   **b.** murky   **c.** aesthetic   **d.** comfortable

In this sentence, *gloomy* is a synonym of the missing word, *murky*, and acts as a restatement clue for it.

A **contrast clue** consists of an *antonym* for or a phrase that means the opposite of the missing word. For example:

While Joanie populates her novels with cheerful people, Seamus's stories center on (**saturnine, defunct**) characters.

In this sentence, *cheerful* is an antonym of the missing word, *saturnine*. This fact is confirmed by the presence of the word *While*, which indicates that the answer must be the opposite of *cheerful*.

An **inference clue** implies but does not directly state the meaning of the missing word or words. For example:

Because Lucius's work was always _____ and never had errors, the teacher gave his essays only a _____ glance before moving onto more time-consuming papers handed in by his classmates.

a. impeccable . . . perfunctory   **c.** pusillanimous . . . sylvan
b. picayune . . . lackadaisical   **d.** vituperative . . . sumptuous

There are a few inference clues in this sentence. The phrase *never had errors* indicates that Lucius's work was flawless, or *impeccable*. The word *glance* suggests that the attention the teacher gave the paper was *perfunctory*. These words are inference clues because they suggest or imply, but do not directly state, the missing words.

VOCABULARY STRATEGY: Word Structure

Prefixes, **suffixes**, and **roots**, or **bases**, are word parts. One strategy for determining an unknown word's meaning is to "take apart" the word and think about the parts. Study the prefixes and suffixes below to help you find out the meanings of words in which they appear

Prefix	Meaning	Sample Words
com-, con-	together, with	compatriot, contact
de-, dis-	lower, opposite	devalue, disloyal
il-, im-, in-, ir, non-, un-	not	illegal, impossible, inactive, irregular, nonsense, unable
super-	above, greater than	superimpose, superstar

Noun Suffix	Meaning	Sample Nouns
-acy, -ance, -ence, -hood, -ity, -ment, -ness, -ship	state, quality, or condition of, act or process of	adequacy, attendance, persistence, neighborhood, activity, judgment, brightness, friendship
-ant, -eer, -ent, -er, -ian, -ier, -ist, -or	one who does or makes something	contestant, auctioneer, resident, banker, comedian, financier, dentist, doctor
-ation, -ition, -ion	act or result of	organization, imposition, election

Verb Suffix	Meaning	Sample Verbs
-ate	to become, produce, or treat	validate, salivate, chlorinate
-fy, -ify, -ize	to cause, make	liquefy, glorify, legalize

Adjective Suffix	Meaning	Sample Adjectives
-al, -ic,	relating to, characteristic of	natural, romantic
-ful, -ive, -ous	full of, given to, marked by	beautiful, protective, poisonous

A **base** or **root** is the main part of a word to which prefixes and suffixes may be added. On the Classical Roots page of the Word Study section, you will learn more about Latin and Greek roots and the English words that derive from them. The following lists may help you figure out the meaning of new or unfamiliar words.

Greek Root	Meaning	Sample Words
-cryph-, -crypt-	hidden, secret	apocryphal, cryptographer
-dem-, -demo-	people	epidemic, democracy
-gen-	race, kind, origin, birth	generation
-gnos-	know	diagnostic
-lys-	break down	analysis

Latin Root	Meaning	Sample Words
-cap-, -capt-, -cept-, -cip-	take	capitulate, captive, concept, recipient
-cede-, -ceed-, -ceas- -cess-	happen, yield, go	precede, proceed, decease, cessation
-fac-, -fact-, -fect-, -fic-, -fy-	make	faculty, artifact, defect, beneficial, clarify
-tac-, -tag-, -tang-, -teg-	touch	contact, contagious, tangible, integral
-tain-, -ten-, -tin-	hold, keep	contain, tenure, retinue

For more prefixes, suffixes, and roots, visit **vocabularyworkshop.com**.

VOCABULARY AND READING

Word knowledge is essential to reading comprehension. Your knowledge of word meanings and ability to think carefully about what you read will help you succeed in school and on standardized tests, including the SAT, the ACT, and the PSAT.

New **Reading Passages** provide extra practice with vocabulary words. Vocabulary words are boldfaced to draw students' attention to their uses and contexts. Context clues embedded in the passages encourage students to figure out the meanings of words before they read the definitions provided on the pages directly following the passages.

Students read excerpts from classic literature in the **Vocabulary in Context** exercises. Each excerpt includes one of the Unit vocabulary words as it is used in the original work. Students can use what they learn about the word from its use in context to answer questions on the definition.

The **Vocabulary for Comprehension** exercises in each review consist of a nonfiction reading passage followed by comprehension questions. The passages and questions are similar to those that you are likely to find on standardized tests.

Kinds of Questions

Main Idea Questions generally ask what the passage as a whole is about. Often, but not always, the main idea is stated in the first paragraph of the passage. You may also be asked the main idea of a specific paragraph. Questions about the main idea may begin like this:

- The primary or main purpose of the passage is. . .
- The passage is best described as. . .
- The title that best describes the content of the passage is. . .

Detail Questions focus on important information that is explicitly stated in the passage. Often, however, the correct answer choices do not use the exact language of the passage. They are instead restatements, or paraphrases, of the text.

Vocabulary-in-Context Questions check your ability to use context to identify a word's meaning. Use line references to see how and in what context the word is used. For example:

- **Badinage** (line 3) is best defined as. . .
- The meaning of **luminous** (line 15) is. . .

Use context to check your answer choices, particularly when the vocabulary word has more than one meaning. Among the choices may be two (or more) correct meanings of the word in question. Choose the meaning that best fits the context.

Inference Questions ask you to make inferences or draw conclusions from the passage. These questions often begin like this:

- It can be inferred from the passage that. . .
- The author implies that. . .
- Evidently the author feels that. . .

The inferences you make and the conclusions you draw must be based on the information in the passage. Your own knowledge and reasoning come into play in understanding what is implied and in reaching conclusions that are logical.

Questions About Tone show your understanding of the author's attitude toward the subject of the passage. Words that describe tone, or attitude, are "feeling" words, such as *indifferent, ambivalent, scornful, astonished, respectful*. These are typical questions:

- The author's attitude toward . . . is best described as. . .
- Which word best describes the author's tone?

To determine the tone, pay attention to the author's word choice. The author's attitude may be positive (respectful), negative (scornful), or neutral (ambivalent).

Questions About Author's Technique focus on the way a text is organized and the language the author uses. These questions ask you to think about structure and function. For example:

- The final paragraph serves to. . .
- The author cites . . . in order to . . . .

To answer the questions, you must demonstrate an understanding of the way the author presents information and develops ideas.

Strategies

Here are some general strategies to help you as you read each passage and answer the questions.

- Read the introduction first. The introduction will provide a focus for the selection.

- Be an active reader. As you read, ask yourself questions about the passage—for example: What is this paragraph about? What does the writer mean here? Why does the writer include this information?

- Refer to the passage when you answer the questions. In general, the order of the questions mirrors the organization of the passage, and many of the questions include paragraph or line references. It is often helpful to go back and reread before choosing an answer.

- Read carefully, and be sure to base your answer choices on the passage. There are answer choices that make sense but are not based on the information in the passage. These are true statements, but they are incorrect answers. The correct answers are either restatements of ideas in the text or inferences that can be drawn from the text.

- Consider each exercise a learning experience. Keep in mind that your ability to answer the questions correctly shows as much about your understanding of the questions as about your understanding of the passage.

WORKING WITH ANALOGIES

A verbal analogy expresses a relationship or comparison between sets of words. Normally, an analogy contains two pairs of words linked by a word or symbol that stands for an equal (=) sign. A complete analogy compares the two pairs of words and makes a statement about them. It asserts that the relationship between the first—or key—pair of words is the same as the relationship between the second pair.

In the **Analogies** exercises in the Final Mastery Test, you will be asked to complete analogies—that is, to choose the pair of words that best matches or parallels the relationship of the key, or given, pair of words. Here are two examples:

1. maple is to **tree** as	**2. joyful** is to **gloomy** as
a. acorn is to oak	**a.** cheerful is to happy
b. hen is to rooster	**b.** strong is to weak
c. rose is to flower	**c.** quick is to famous
d. shrub is to lilac	**d.** hungry is to starving

In order to find the correct answer to exercise 1, you must first determine the relationship between the two key words, **maple** and **tree**. In this case, that relationship might be expressed as "a maple is a kind (or type) of tree." The next step is to select from choices a, b, c, and d the pair of words that best reflects the same relationship. The correct answer is (c); it is the only pair whose relationship parallels the one in the key words: A rose is a kind (or type) of flower, just as a maple is a kind (or type) of tree. The other choices do not express the same relationship.

In exercise 2, the relationship between the key words can be expressed as "joyful means the opposite of gloomy." Which of the choices best represents the same relationship? The answer is (b): "strong means the opposite of weak."

Here are examples of some other common analogy relationships:

Analogy	Key Relationship
big is to **large** as **little** is to **small**	**Big** means the same thing as **large**, just as **little** means the same thing as **small**.
brave is to **favorable** as **cowardly** is to **unfavorable**	The tone of **brave** is **favorable**, just as the tone of **cowardly** is **unfavorable**.
busybody is to **nosy** as **klutz** is to **clumsy**	A **busybody** is by definition someone who is **nosy**, just as a **klutz** is by definition someone who is **clumsy**.
cowardly is to **courage** as **awkward** is to **grace**	Someone who is **cowardly** lacks **courage**, just as someone who is **awkward** lacks **grace**.
visible is to **see** as **audible** is to **hear**	If something is **visible**, you can by definition **see** it, just as if something is **audible**, you can by definition **hear** it.
liar is to **truthful** as **bigot** is to **fair-minded**	A **liar** is by definition not likely to be **truthful**, just as a **bigot** is by definition not likely to be **fair-minded**.
eyes are to **see** as **ears** are to **hear**	You use your **eyes** to **see** with, just as you use your **ears** to **hear** with.

There are many different kinds of relationships represented in the analogy questions you will find in the Final Mastery Test, but the key to solving any analogy is to find and express the relationship between the two key words.

*Read the following selection, taking note of the **boldface** words and their contexts. These words are among those you will be studying in Unit 1. As you complete the exercises in this unit, it may help to refer to the way the words are used below.*

Across the Pond

<Letters>

January 27, 1891

My Dear Cora,

Accept my congratulations on the establishment of the National American Women's Suffrage Association. Am I too bold to presume this new unity in the American suffrage movement marks the end of the **invidious** divisions in your ranks? English appetite for American news is **insatiable** of late, with much talk of means by which we might **emulate** your recent achievements. Just yesterday, at a small gathering of friends of our League, I heard Mrs. Pankhurst break off into a rousing **encomium** on the entry of the state of Wyoming into your union. The opinion here is that with one state now granting universal suffrage, it's only a matter of time before the dam breaks.

In England we persuade ourselves to **eschew** hope for such grand achievements till the times make them more **tenable**. There's plenty of work to be done to prepare for the event. The Pankhursts have inspired many of us to push for the women's vote in local elections. This would be no small thing in itself, and should help our effort to reform the conservative spirit of our country. I fear the climate in America is more favorable to the endeavor, while opposition here remains **intransigent**. At tea not long ago, I heard one Mr. Evans produce the most **banal** argument against the women's vote you could

imagine. I won't trouble you with details of his **carping** rhetoric, but note that he took pains to demonstrate that women are "unfit for the public duties of citizenship," and greatly feared the prospect that women's votes might "swamp the votes of men." Imagine my delight when, pressed by objections from several present, the good Mr. Evans grew suddenly **taciturn**, and at a loss for any other means of **temporizing**, complimented his hostess and bid us good day!

Charles and I often recall your kindness during our last visit, and look forward to seeing you again this summer.

Affectionately,

Millicent

March 20, 1891

Dearest Millie,

We have many like your Mr. Evans here, which puts our own work ahead of us. I can, however, **substantiate** your optimism where Wyoming is concerned. Other Western states and territories will surely follow suit, with energy already in the project in Idaho, Colorado, and elsewhere. Women's suffrage has firmer roots in the West, and we expect more progress there.

Germane to the topic, I had the privilege of meeting Jane Addams in Chicago, where she has founded the Hull House, devoted to the education of local women of the working class. Miss Addams is a remarkable woman, and strikes me as the very type to carry our movement forward. Initial renovations of the Hull Mansion were funded primarily through her own **largesse**, and she has become an advocate for local suffrage in Chicago and for other progressive causes.

Our new Association might show the extent to which the old arguments that divided us have passed into history, but new excuses for dissent emerge as old ones fade. The new tendency to portray women as "domestic" spirits, superior in moral virtue to men, strikes some of us as misguided. I'll not **belabor** the point here, hoping instead to present a **coherent** argument for you in person when you arrive in New York.

Until then, I keep you in my thoughts. Your friend always,

Cora

iWords

Snap the code, or go to
vocabularyworkshop.com

Jane Addams

American women fought for the right to vote in each state, until the Nineteenth Amendment was passed in 1920.

Definitions

Note the spelling, pronunciation, part(s) of speech, and definition(s) of each of the following words. Then write the word in the blank spaces in the illustrative sentence(s) following. Finally, study the lists of synonyms and antonyms.

1. acquisitive
(ə kwiz′ ə tiv)

(*adj.*) able to get and retain ideas or information; concerned with acquiring wealth or property

In an _____ society, there is a great deal of emphasis on buying and selling.

SYNONYMS: greedy, avaricious, retentive
ANTONYM: altruistic

2. arrogate
(a′ rə gāt)

(*v.*) to claim or take without right

The ambitious noblemen will put the young king under house arrest and _____ royal privileges to themselves.

SYNONYMS: expropriate, commandeer
ANTONYMS: renounce, abdicate, abandon

3. banal
(bə nal′)

(*adj.*) hackneyed, trite, commonplace

The new play's _____ dialogue made it seem more like a soap opera than a serious drama.

SYNONYMS: stale, insipid
ANTONYMS: fresh, original, new

4. belabor
(bi lā′ bər)

(*v.*) to work on excessively; to thrash soundly

His tendency to _____ the small points often made him miss the big picture.

SYNONYM: overwork

5. carping
(kär′ piŋ)

(*adj.*) tending to find fault, especially in a petty, nasty, or hairsplitting way; (*n.*) petty, nagging criticism

The trainee resigned after a week rather than put up with the _____ complaints of the sales manager.

Most artists choose to ignore the _____ of critics and simply go on with their work.

SYNONYMS: (*adj.*) nit-picking, caviling
ANTONYMS: (*adj.*) approving, uncritical

6. coherent
(kō hēr′ ənt)

(*adj.*) holding or sticking together; making a logical whole; comprehensible, meaningful

The physics teacher gave a surprisingly _____ description of quantum mechanics.

SYNONYMS: connected, unified, consistent, cohesive
ANTONYMS: muddled, chaotic, disjointed

7. congeal
(kən jēl')

(*v.*) to change from liquid to solid, thicken; to make inflexible or rigid

If you do not wash your dishes right away, the food on them will _____.

SYNONYMS: harden, jell, solidify
ANTONYM: liquefy

8. emulate
(em' yə lāt)

(*v.*) to imitate with the intent of equaling or surpassing the model

Most beginning writers try to _____ a great writer and later develop their own individual styles.

SYNONYMS: copy, mimic, rival, match, measure up to

9. encomium
(en kō' mē əm)

(*n.*) a formal expression of praise, a lavish tribute

On Veterans Day, the President delivered a heartfelt _____ to those who died for their country.

SYNONYMS: panegyric, eulogy
ANTONYMS: condemnation, castigation, criticism

10. eschew
(es chü')

(*v.*) to avoid, shun, keep away from

The young athletes promised the coach that they would train vigorously and _____ bad habits.

SYNONYMS: abstain from, steer clear of, forgo
ANTONYMS: embrace, adopt

11. germane
(jər mān')

(*adj.*) relevant, appropriate, apropos, fitting

Bringing up examples from the past is not _____ to the present discussion.

SYNONYM: pertinent
ANTONYMS: irrelevant, extraneous, inappropriate

12. insatiable
(in sā' shə bəl)

(*adj.*) so great or demanding as not to be satisfied

People with an _____ appetite for gossip often do not have compelling stories of their own.

SYNONYMS: unquenchable, ravenous

13. intransigent
(in tran' sə jənt)

(*adj.*) refusing to compromise, irreconcilable

Little will get accomplished if the legislators of both parties maintain their _____ attitudes.

SYNONYMS: uncompromising, unyielding, obdurate
ANTONYMS: lukewarm, halfhearted, yielding

14. invidious
(in vid′ ē əs)

(*adj.*) offensive, hateful; tending to cause bitterness and resentment

Bosses should avoid making _____ comparisons between their employees.

SYNONYMS: malicious, spiteful, prejudicial, pejorative
ANTONYMS: flattering, ameliorative

15. largesse
(lär jes′)

(*n.*) generosity in giving; lavish or bountiful contributions

The university was the fortunate beneficiary of the _____ of many of its graduates.

SYNONYMS: liberality, bounty
ANTONYMS: stinginess, miserliness, niggardliness

16. reconnaissance
(ri kän′ ə səns)

(*n.*) a survey made for military purposes; any kind of preliminary inspection or examination

The field officer required a thorough _____ before ordering any troop movements.

SYNONYM: exploration

17. substantiate
(səb stan′ shē āt)

(*v.*) to establish by evidence, prove; to give concrete or substantial form to

The prospector was unable to _____ his claim to the land where the gold was found.

SYNONYMS: confirm, validate, authenticate
ANTONYMS: refute, disprove, invalidate

✳ **18. taciturn**
(tas′ ə tərn)

(*adj.*) habitually silent or quiet, inclined to talk very little

Woodrow Wilson has the reputation of having a dour and _____ personality.

SYNONYMS: tight-lipped, uncommunicative, laconic
ANTONYMS: garrulous, loquacious, prolix, verbose

19. temporize
(tem′ pə rīz)

(*v.*) to stall or act evasively in order to gain time, avoid a confrontation, or postpone a decision; to compromise

For most of Shakespeare's great tragedy, the protagonist Hamlet chooses to _____ rather than act.

SYNONYMS: dillydally, procrastinate

20. tenable
(ten′ ə bəl)

(*adj.*) capable of being held or defended

The researchers put forth a _____ theory, but their conclusions would be reviewed carefully by others.

SYNONYMS: defensible, justifiable, maintainable
ANTONYMS: indefensible, unjustifiable

Choosing the Right Word

*Select the **boldface** word that better completes each sentence. You might refer to the selection on pages 12–13 to see how most of these words are used in context.*

1. Famous for his monosyllabic replies to questions and a somber and (**taciturn**, germane) nature, President Coolidge had the nickname "Silent Cal."

2. In that moment of grief, the conventional expressions of sympathy I had always considered (tenable, **banal**) were surprisingly comforting.

3. I am proud to have it said of me that I am stubborn and (invidious, **intransigent**) when genuine moral issues are involved.

4. Ethelred the Unready was so reluctant to face the Vikings who invaded his kingdom that in effect he (arrogated, **temporized**) himself off the throne.

5. What evidence can you offer to (**substantiate**, eschew) the assertion that capital punishment does not deter potential murderers?

UNITED STATES POSTAGE

$5 CALVIN COOLIDGE 1923-1929 $5

Stamp issued in 1938 to honor Calvin Coolidge, the thirtieth President of the United States.

6. Suddenly a band of ruffians set upon us and began to (congeal, **belabor**) us with blows and curses.

7. Even a very imperfect human being may sometimes have virtues of mind or character that are worthy of (carping, **emulation**).

8. Aristotle had such a(n) (tenable, **acquisitive**) mind that his writings are a veritable gold mine of odd and interesting information.

9. The mood of easy cordiality with which we began the meeting soon (**congealed**, temporized) into icy politeness.

10. The poor woman was in such a state of shock after the accident that she couldn't give a (**coherent**, taciturn) account of what had happened.

11. The new batting champion in our softball league is a(n) (insatiable, **taciturn**) young man who prefers to let his bat do his talking for him.

12. The speech was so filled with (**encomiums**, reconnaissance) that I found it hard to believe that the subject of all this acclaim was plain old me.

13. "That word has such (**invidious**, germane) connotations in modern American parlance," I said, "that I would hesitate to use it, even in jest."

14. His figure bears witness to his (acquisitive, **insatiable**) appetite for the pleasures of the table.

15. In our attempt to improve the quality of life in America, we should not be too quick to (**eschew**, cohere) old ideas simply because they are old.

16. When the evidence of his misconduct became irrefutable, he saw that his position was not (**banal, tenable**) and resigned.

17. After the editor read the story, he returned it to the author with only a few (**carping, coherent**) criticisms of minor faults penciled in the margin.

18. The Constitution is uniquely designed to provide protection against those who might seek to (**substantiate, arrogate**) undue power to themselves.

19. Aerial (**reconnaissance, encomium**) of the enemy's positions provided the general with the information he needed to plan his attack.

20. After I mowed the lawn for an hour, he gave me a whole dollar with the air of a feudal lord bestowing (**largesse, intransigence**) on a grateful serf.

21. Your critical comments about my "lack of social background" may be true, but they are not (**coherent, germane**) to my qualifications for office.

22. Because this committee has (**belabored, emulated**) the issue of zoning laws for months, we will not invite public comments on it again in tonight's meeting.

23. The historian needed to scrutinize additional handwriting samples before he could (**eschew, substantiate**) the signature on the document.

24. Instead of opening voters' minds to new ideas, the debate actually (**arrogated, congealed**) their previous objections to the proposed legislation.

25. The (**carping, largesse**) of grateful patients made the clinic's expansion possible.

Synonyms

*Choose the word from this unit that is the same or most nearly the same in meaning as the **boldface** word or expression in the phrase. Write that word on the line. Use a dictionary if necessary.*

1. **harp on** the same point again and again — *carping*

2. the **grasping** real estate developer — *acquisitive*

3. tried to **usurp** control of the finances — *arrogate*

4. tends to **hedge** when confronted by direct questions — *eschew*

5. the puppy's **voracious** hunger — *insatiable*

6. led the **scouting expedition** into the jungle — *reconnaissance*

7. was thanked for her **munificence** — *largesse*

8. could not **verify** the alibi — *substantiate*

9. received a well-deserved **commendation** — *encomium*

10. blood that does not **coagulate** — *congeal*

Antonyms

*Choose the word from this unit that is most nearly opposite in meaning to the **boldface** word or expression in the phrase. Write that word on the line. Use a dictionary if necessary.*

1. made a very **magnanimous** remark _____

2. an **unretentive** mind that cannot remember details _____

3. the **inspired** lyrics to that song _____

4. mayor who tries to **relinquish** power _____

5. butter that does not **soften** _____

Completing the Sentence

From the words in this unit, choose the one that best completes each of the following sentences. Write the word in the space provided.

1. Some of the episodes in the series were wonderfully fresh and original; others were just plain ____*banal*____.

2. I don't object to the inclusion of anecdotes in a serious lecture, but they should at the very least be ____*germane*____ to the subject.

3. There is nothing wrong with ____*emulating*____ the great singers of the past as long as you eventually develop a style that is all your own.

4. When the temperature outside dropped suddenly, the muddy water in the ditch ____*congeal*____ into a mass of icy sludge.

5. The purpose of military ____*reconnaissance*____ remains the same whether cavalry or helicopters are used: to learn as much as possible about the enemy.

6. In any crisis, the longer a person ____*temporizes*____, the greater the danger is likely to become.

7. In spite of his size, he was so ____*taciturn*____ that we tended to forget that he was even in the room.

8. The novel contains an interesting study of a miser's ____*insatiable*____ lust for gold and its evil effects on those around him.

9. By whose authority did you ____*arrogate*____ to yourself the right to decide how the club's money would be spent?

10. She received housing vouchers and food stamps as a result of the government's ____*largesse*____.

11. Students who seek high grades must learn to _eschew_ the joys of that one-eyed monster, the television.

12. "There is no need for you to _belabor_ the point," I replied, "when I already understand clearly what your criticism is."

13. As a result of recent research, earlier theories about the origin of the universe are no longer _tenable_.

14. I doubt very much that he can _substantiate_ his assertion that he won two gold medals in the 1956 Olympics.

15. In my opinion, there is absolutely no justification for making such _invidious_ distinctions between the two types of product.

16. Your essay would be a great deal tighter and more _coherent_ if you removed all the extraneous information it now contains.

17. How can we "meet them halfway" when they are so _intransigent_ in their opposition to what we propose to do?

18. Even the most severe critics showered _encomium_ on the young writer for the remarkable narrative power of her first novel.

19. Never having any money in one's pockets can be a real trial for someone born with the _acquisitive_ instincts of a pack rat.

20. Despite the _carping_ and nit-picking of a few petty minds, I feel we have substantially improved our local school system of late.

Writing: Words in Action

1. Look back at "Across the Pond" (pages 12–13). Suppose you are Cora's friend and a fellow member of the National American Women's Suffrage Association. You want to persuade men in the Western states that women should have the right to vote. Write a persuasive essay, using at least two details from the passage and three unit words to support your argument.

2. *"A long habit of not thinking a thing wrong gives it a superficial appearance of being right." —Thomas Paine*

   Do you agree with Paine's statement? In a brief essay, explain your opinion with specific examples from your studies, reading (refer to pages 12–13), personal observations and experience, or current events. Write at least three paragraphs, and use three or more words from this unit.

Vocabulary in Context

Literary Text

The following excerpts are from Charlotte Brontë's novels The Professor *and* Shirley. *Some of the words you have studied in this unit appear in* **boldface** *type. Complete each statement below the excerpt by circling the letter of the correct answer.*

1. I had the conviction that he could only regard me as a poor-spirited slave, wherefore I now went about to shun his presence and **eschew** his conversation. *(The Professor)*

To **eschew** is to

  a. repudiate   **c.** ridicule
  b. clarify   **d.** avoid

2. In the course of my next lesson, I made a report of the other devoirs, dealing out praise and blame in very small retail parcels, according to my custom, for there was no use in blaming severely, and high **encomiums** were rarely merited. *(The Professor)*

Encomiums are

  a. expectations   **c.** successes
  b. tributes   **d.** condemnations

3. For a day or two Mr. Sympson continued as bland as oil, but also he seemed to sit on pins, and his gait, when he walked, **emulated** that of a hen treading a hot girdle. *(Shirley)*

Something that is **emulated** is

  a. foreshadowed   **c.** spurned
  b. fabricated   **d.** imitated

4. "The faults of my manner are, I think, only negative. I am not proud. What has a man in my position to be proud of? I am only **taciturn,** phlegmatic, and joyless." *(Shirley)*

Someone who is **taciturn** is NOT

  a. loquacious   **c.** serious
  b. quiet   **d.** ironic

5. But what has been said in the last page or two is not **germane** to Caroline Helstone's feelings, or to the state of things between her and Robert Moore. *(Shirley)*

If something is **germane**, it is

  a. sympathetic   **c.** worthwhile
  b. relevant   **d.** reassuring

Charlotte Brontë published several novels under the male pen name Currer Bell.

Interactive Quiz

Snap the code, or go to **vocabularyworkshop.com**

*Read the following selection, taking note of the **boldface** words and their contexts. These words are among those you will be studying in Unit 2. As you complete the exercises in this unit, it may help to refer to the way the words are used below.*

Constructing the New York City Subway
<Historical Nonfiction>

By 1900, nearly four million people lived in New York City, about five times as many as had lived in the same area fifty years earlier. The **celerity** of the population's increase was driven by a range of factors including economic growth, industrialization, and immigration. As an **overt** symptom of the prosperity of the city and the nation, rapid population growth was welcomed by many of the city's inhabitants. But the increase in population posed serious challenges. **Myopic** disregard for the supply of housing left many of the city's poorer inhabitants crammed into crowded tenements until construction began to keep pace. And the growing mass of people traveling throughout the city created unprecedented amounts of traffic in the streets.

Traffic congestion swelled beyond the bounds of **propriety**. Traffic accidents were all too common, as drivers of horse-drawn omnibuses, in a rush to pick up passengers and earn fares, saw fit to trample pedestrians along the way. Street traffic was a constant target of **animadversion** in the press. But it was also a cause of innovation. As the streams of pedestrians and horse-drawn carriages grew steadily through the nineteenth century, railroads were elevated above street level to avoid interference with the **maelstrom** of traffic on the streets. Steam-powered elevated railways were soon replaced by cleaner electric-powered elevated lines.

Plans for building a subway had been drawn as early as the 1860s, but the project was stalled for decades by **devious** local politics. Operators of surface railways and horse-drawn cars, who feared competition from the subway, cast the plan in a **pejorative** light, claiming

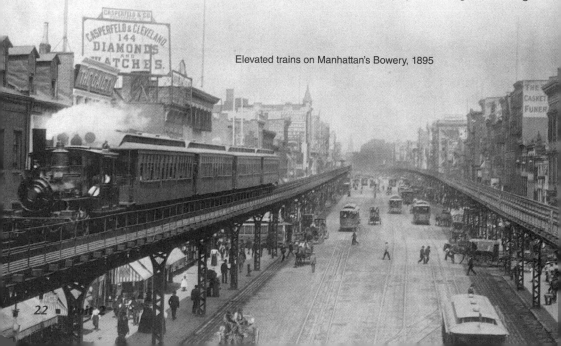

Elevated trains on Manhattan's Bowery, 1895

Left: Subway construction, 1902; Below: Vintage NYC subway, 2004

it was impractical and bound to fail. The **suppliant** protests of property owners who worried that prolonged subway construction would interfere with business helped strengthen opposition to the subway. **Avid** supporters of the subway plan, on the other hand, considered any opposition to be **sacrilege**. But adversity will not last forever. In the end, the clear benefits that the subway would bring to the city by increasing the speed of transit and by alleviating the traffic on the streets proved more compelling than the political **gambits** employed by opponents. After decades of false starts, **incendiary** rhetoric, and **histrionic** arguments on both sides, a contract for construction was signed on February 21, 1900. Construction began **summarily** in the following months.

Thousands of laborers worked on the project. Most of the tunnels were built using the "cut-and-cover" method: Workers dug trenches through the streets and covered them with wooden planks and bridges to allow traffic to pass overhead while work continued. Down in the trenches, workers laid the tracks, built the subway stations, and surrounded the subway with steel and concrete. Then they rebuilt the street above. The construction company that built the subway was also responsible for building the coal-fueled generators that would produce the subway's electricity.

The subway opened to the public on October 27, 1904. About 150,000 people stood in line to pay the five-cent fare for a rocky, **undulating** ride on what was then the fastest public transportation system in the world. Over the next few decades, the city's subway system was expanded and integrated with the elevated lines above ground. An impressive feat of engineering for its time, the New York City subway system remains one of the largest in the world to this day.

iWords

Snap the code, or go to **vocabularyworkshop.com**

Definitions

Note the spelling, pronunciation, part(s) of speech, and definition(s) of each of the following words. Then write the word in the blank spaces in the illustrative sentence(s) following. Finally, study the lists of synonyms and antonyms.

1. accost
(ə käst′)

(v.) to approach and speak to first; to confront in a challenging or aggressive way

The nobleman was _____ by beggars on his way to the castle.

SYNONYMS: buttonhole, approach
ANTONYMS: avoid, shun

2. animadversion
(an ə mad vər′ zhən)

(n.) a comment indicating strong criticism or disapproval

The inexperienced filmmaker was disheartened by the _____ of the film critic.

SYNONYMS: rebuke, reproof
ANTONYMS: praise, compliment

3. avid
(av′ id)

(adj.) desirous of something to the point of greed; intensely eager

Most writers are also _____ readers who have loved books since childhood.

SYNONYMS: keen, enthusiastic, grasping
ANTONYMS: reluctant, indifferent, unenthusiastic

4. brackish
(brak′ ish)

(adj.) having a salty taste and unpleasant to drink

The shipwrecked passengers adrift on the lifeboat became ill after drinking _____ water.

SYNONYM: saline
ANTONYMS: clear, sweet

5. celerity
(sə ler′ ə tē)

(n.) swiftness, rapidity of motion or action

Although the heavy snowfall was not expected, the highway department responded with surprising _____.

SYNONYMS: promptness, speed
ANTONYMS: slowness, sluggishness, dilatoriness

6. devious
(dē′ vē əs)

(adj.) straying or wandering from a straight or direct course; done or acting in a shifty or underhanded way

The interrogator used _____ methods to try to get the suspect to incriminate himself.

SYNONYMS: roundabout, indirect, tricky, sly, artful
ANTONYMS: direct, straightforward, open, aboveboard

7. gambit
(gam' bit)

(*n.*) in chess, an opening move that involves risk or sacrifice of a minor piece in order to gain a later advantage; any opening move of this type

Asking an interesting stranger about his or her job is a popular party _____.

SYNONYMS: ploy, ruse, maneuver

8. halcyon
(hal' sē ən)

(*n.*) a legendary bird identified with the kingfisher; (*adj.*) of or relating to the halcyon; calm, peaceful; happy, golden; prosperous, affluent

The teacher read the legend of the _____, a mythic bird that nested in a calm sea.

The woman often spoke of the _____ days of her childhood.

SYNONYMS: (*adj.*) tranquil, placid, palmy
ANTONYMS: (*adj.*) turbulent, tumultuous

9. histrionic
(his trē än' ik)

(*adj.*) pertaining to actors and their techniques; theatrical, artificial; melodramatic

Upon receiving his award, the young actor gave a _____ speech.

SYNONYMS: affected, stagy
ANTONYMS: muted, untheatrical, subdued

10. Incendiary
(in sen' dē er ē)

(*adj.*) deliberately setting or causing fires; designed to start fires; tending to stir up strife or rebellion; (*n.*) one who deliberately sets fires, arsonist; one who causes strife

The arsonist planted an _____ device in the basement of the store.

The radical _____ was sentenced to life imprisonment.

SYNONYMS: (*adj.*) inflammatory, provocative; (*n.*) firebrand
ANTONYMS: (*adj.*) soothing, quieting; (*n.*) peacemaker

11. maelstrom
(māl' strəm)

(*n.*) a whirlpool of great size and violence; a situation resembling a whirlpool in violence and destruction

Many innocent people caught in the _____ of the revolution lost their lives and property.

SYNONYMS: chaos, turbulence, tumult

12. myopic
(mī äp' ik)

(*adj.*) nearsighted; lacking a broad, realistic view of a situation; lacking foresight or discernment

The _____ foreign policy of the last administration has led to serious problems with our allies.

SYNONYM: shortsighted
ANTONYM: farsighted

13. overt
(ō vert′)

(*adj.*) open, not hidden, expressed or revealed in a way that is easily recognized

In order for Congress to declare war, the President must demonstrate an _____ threat.

SYNONYMS: clear, obvious, manifest, patent
ANTONYMS: clandestine, covert, concealed

14. pejorative
(pə jôr′ ə tiv)

(*adj.*) tending to make worse; expressing disapproval or disparagement, derogatory, deprecatory, belittling

The lawyer was accused of making a _____ remark when referring to the defendant's background.

ANTONYMS: complimentary, ameliorative

15. propriety
(prə prī′ ə tē)

(*n.*) the state of being proper, appropriateness; (*pl.*) standards of what is proper or socially acceptable

The social worker questioned the _____ of the police's request to see confidential records.

SYNONYMS: fitness, correctness
ANTONYMS: unseemliness, inappropriateness

16. sacrilege
(sak′ rə lij)

(*n.*) improper or disrespectful treatment of something held sacred

The anthropologist was accused of committing a _____ when she disturbed a burial ground.

SYNONYMS: desecration, profanation, defilement

17. summarily
(sə mer′ ə lē)

(*adv.*) without delay or formality; briefly, concisely

As soon as there was evidence of criminal wrongdoing, the official was _____ ousted from his post.

SYNONYMS: promptly, peremptorily

18. suppliant
(səp′ lē ənt)

(*adj.*) asking humbly and earnestly; (*n.*) one who makes a request humbly and earnestly, a petitioner, suitor

He made a _____ address to the parole board.

Stranded in the deserted city of Moscow, Napoleon had to turn to the Czar not as a conqueror but as a _____.

19. talisman
(tal′ iz mən)

(*n.*) an object that serves as a charm or is believed to confer magical powers, an amulet, fetish

Most people do not believe that rabbit's feet and other _____ actually bring good luck.

20. undulate
(ən′ dyə lāt)

(*v.*) to move in waves or with a wavelike motion; to have a wavelike appearance or form

The baseball fans began to _____ as they cheered, so that they appeared to move in a wave.

SYNONYMS: fluctuate, rise and fall

Choosing the Right Word

Select the **boldface** word that better completes each sentence. You might refer to the selection on pages 22–23 to see how most of these words are used in context.

1. In ancient Egypt, (**talismans**, **sacrileges**) with the image of a scarab beetle were considered sacred and believed to have healing and protective powers.

2. The infatuated schoolboy, in one of his more restrained expressions, described himself as "a (**sacrilege**, **suppliant**) at the altar of love."

3. "I realize that this kind of financial (**gambit**, **sacrilege**) has its risks," she said, "but I expect it to pay off handsomely in the end."

4. "His acts of defiance have been so (**myopic**, **overt**) and premeditated that I have no choice but to fire him," she said sadly.

5. John Masefield's poem "Sea Fever" has an (**avid**, **undulating**) rhythm that actually gives one the feeling of being on a rolling ship.

The scarab beetle on this gold bracelet symbolized rebirth to ancient Egyptians.

6. Walt tends to react slowly, but when he feels that his own interests are at stake he can move with striking (**celerity**, **myopia**).

7. Although all politicians must have some ability to dramatize themselves, it is very easy to overdo the (**proprieties**, **histrionics**).

8. The adoring fan regarded my negative comments about his favorite singer as tantamount to (**maelstrom**, **sacrilege**).

9. Without even considering the new evidence that I was prepared to present, they (**deviously**, **summarily**) denied my appeal to reopen the case.

10. She was buffeted about in a veritable (**gambit**, **maelstrom**) of emotions, caused mainly by her own dissatisfaction with herself.

11. He regarded his Phi Beta Kappa key as a(n) (**talisman**, **animadversion**) that would open all doors and win him universal acceptance.

12. He is the kind of person who is concerned not with real moral values but simply with appearances and (**propriety**, **celerity**).

13. Nary a ripple disturbed the (**halcyon**, **brackish**) calm of the sea on that glorious summer's afternoon.

14. Instead of imbibing the (**brackish**, **suppliant**) waters of superstition, let us refresh ourselves with long drafts of pure, clean common sense.

15. Because the word *appeasement* is associated with disastrous concessions to Adolf Hitler, it has acquired a(n) (**pejorative**, **overt**) connotation.

either works
↙ ↘

16. His reckless words had an (**incendiary, overt**) effect on the already excited crowd, and large-scale rioting resulted.

17. As the defendant left the courtroom, he was (**gambited, accosted**) by a group of reporters seeking his reaction to the verdict.

18. I certainly do not claim that my performance in office was beyond criticism, but I deeply resent (**animadversions, maelstroms**) on my honesty.

19. After years of failure to sell a single story, the young writer described himself bitterly as "a(n) (**pejorative, avid**) collector of rejection slips."

20. In an age when the United States has truly global responsibilities, we can ill afford leaders with (**myopic, pejorative**) points of view.

21. His methods were so complicated and his purposes so (**avid, devious**) that we were not sure if he was spying on the enemy or on us.

22. As reported in several online news sites, the (**incendiary, gambit**) accused in the destructive forest fires has admitted his guilt.

23. To the delight of the impatient graduates, the university president offered her comments at the commencement ceremony (**summarily, brackishly**).

24. After the young actor's audition, the casting directors delivered a harsh evaluation of his overly (**histrionic, undulating**) monologue.

25. My (**myopic, suppliant**) request for a later curfew proved successful.

Synonyms

*Choose the word from this unit that is the same or most nearly the same in meaning as the **boldface** word or expression in the phrase. Write that word on the line. Use a dictionary if necessary.*

1. a lucky **amulet** _____

2. the **vortex** of public opinion _____

3. **ripple** in the current _____

4. was taken in by her **stratagem** _____

5. swam in the **briny** water _____

6. **abruptly** resigned from the Cabinet _____

7. behaved with her usual **decorum** _____

8. memories of our **serene** beginnings _____

9. **confronted** the thief at the door _____

10. completed the job with **alacrity** _____

Antonyms

*Choose the word from this unit that is most nearly opposite in meaning to the **boldface** word or expression in the phrase. Write that word on the line. Use a dictionary if necessary.*

1. a pool of **fresh** water. _____

2. made a very **low-keyed** plea for mercy _____

3. **evade** the nosy neighbor _____

4. described the **chaotic** surroundings _____

5. took **secret** action to avoid a crisis _____

Completing the Sentence

From the words in this unit, choose the one that best completes each of the following sentences. Write the word in the space provided.

1. Many a rich southern planter saw all his financial resources swallowed up in the _____maelstrom_____ of the Civil War.

2. Saying that "people who live in glass houses shouldn't throw stones" is not an effective response to their _____animadversion_____ on your conduct.

3. My brother is such a(n) _____avid_____ collector of toy soldiers that I sometimes think our house has been invaded by a pint-sized army.

4. The _____celerity_____ with which he accepted our invitation to dinner suggested that he was badly in need of a good meal.

5. We looked back on those _____halcyon_____ years before the war broke out as a kind of "golden age" in our history.

6. The Japanese attack on Pearl Harbor was a(n) _____overt_____ act of war.

7. His pale face, hunched shoulders, and _____myopic_____ stare showed that he had spent his life poring over old books and documents.

8. To our dismay, we discovered that the water we had worked so hard to bring to the surface was too _____brackish_____ for human consumption.

9. I stand before you an abject _____supplicant_____, hoping against hope for a sign of your forgiveness.

10. In the eyes of most Americans, people who burn or spit on our flag are guilty of a kind of _____sacrilege_____.

11. Down in the main square, a hard-working peasant was selling charms and
_____talisman_____ to ward off the evil eye.

12. After the prisoner had been found guilty of treason, he was led before a firing
squad and __summarily__ executed.

13. In Grandmother's day, standards of __propriety__ required that a young
lady wear a hat and gloves when she went out in public.

14. Any book on chess strategy usually discusses the standard opening moves, such
as the "knight's __gambit__ ."

15. To be really convincing on stage, an opera singer must possess both vocal and
_____histrionic_____ abilities.

16. As an employee of the local polling service last summer, I had to
_____accost_____ people on the street and ask their opinions.

17. The tons of __incendiary__ material ignited and turned the waste
disposal plant into a roaring inferno.

18. The suffix -*ling* often has a(n) __pejorative__ connotation, as in the word
princeling, derived from *prince*.

19. During the rainy season, the highway sank at so many points that its surface
began to __undulate__ like the track for a roller coaster.

20. On the return trip, we cut straight across the meadows rather than take the more
_____devious_____ path along the river.

Writing: Words in Action

1. Look back at "Constructing the New York City Subway" (pages 22–23). Think
about how the completion of the subway changed the lives of city residents.
Write an essay in which you analyze the impact—both positive and negative—
of this new mode of transportation on individuals and businesses in New York
City at the turn of the century. Use at least two details from the passage and
three unit words to support your view.

2. According to a 2005 Gallup Poll, most Americans consider electricity as the
greatest invention of all time, with the automobile and the printing press
ranking well behind. Do you agree? Write an essay of at least three
paragraphs in which you explain what your top choice is and why. Support
your answer with specific examples from your observations, studies, reading
(refer to pages 22–23), or personal experience. Use at least three words
from this unit in your essay.

Vocabulary in Context
Literary Text

The following excerpts are from Theodore Dreiser's novels Sister Carrie *and* Jennie Gerhardt. *Some of the words you have studied in this unit appear in* **boldface** *type. Complete each statement below the excerpt by circling the letter of the correct answer.*

1. For Carrie, as we well know, the stage had a great attraction. She had never forgotten her one **histrionic** achievement in Chicago. *(Sister Carrie)*

Something **histrionic** involves
a. moneymaking   **c.** acting and emotions
b. education   **d.** ambitions and goals

2. Though often disillusioned, she was still waiting for that **halcyon** day when she would be led forth among dreams become real. Ames had pointed out a farther step, but on and on beyond that, if accomplished, would lie others for her. *(Sister Carrie)*

Something that is **halcyon** is NOT
a. peaceful   **c.** happy
b. turbulent   **d.** calm

3. Hanson jumped out of bed with more **celerity** than he usually displayed and looked at the note. *(Sister Carrie)*

Celerity is
a. nervousness   **c.** determination
b. irritability   **d.** swiftness

4. Her support was assured, for her income was paid to her through a trust company. She had no desire for speculation or for the **devious** ways of trade. The care of flowers, the nature of children, the ordering of a home were more in her province. *(Jennie Gerhardt)*

If something is **devious**, it is
a. unhealthy   **c.** respectable
b. shifty   **d.** defiant

The 1952 film *Carrie*, based on Dreiser's novel *Sister Carrie*, stars Laurence Olivier and Jennifer Jones.

5. He had never really been healed of the wound that his father had given him. He had never been comfortable in his mind since Robert had deserted him so **summarily**. *(Jennie Gerhardt)*

Something done **summarily** is done
a. abruptly   **c.** gradually
b. predictably   **d.** sarcastically

Interactive Quiz

Snap the code, or go to **vocabularyworkshop.com**

*Read the following selection, taking note of the **boldface** words and their contexts. These words are among those you will be studying in Unit 3. As you complete the exercises in this unit, it may help to refer to the way the words are used below.*

Third Parties in American Politics
<Encyclopedia Entry>

The two-party system has been in effect since the **primordial** days of American politics and the Founding Fathers. At that time, the two opposing parties were known as the Federalists and the Anti-Federalists. Democrats and Republicans dominate United States politics now, but smaller third parties have addressed **substantive** issues, challenged the two-party orthodoxy, and **evinced** signs of success at local, state, and national levels.

Background and Perspective

A modern-day third-party candidate has yet to wrest the presidency from the Republicans or Democrats. However, many third-party positions have been adopted by the major parties, whose **propinquity** has been **decried** by voters who want clearer divisions.

Sometimes, after Democrats or Republicans have embraced the ideas of a third party, that third party has faded away. Other times—although not since the nineteenth century—a third party has become so powerful that it supplants one of the major parties. This happened in 1856 when the Republican Party, a third party at the time, replaced the Whig Party.

Some third parties have clear-cut platforms and strong nominees, while others have been criticized for **murky** views or **feckless** leadership or for having more **utopian** than real-world positions. Still others are essentially single-issue parties—like the Prohibition Party—known for its opposition to the sale or consumption of alcohol.

Significant Third Parties in U.S. History

The Know-Nothing Party This party rose with **unwonted** rapidity in the mid-1800s. Among other things, its leaders spread **nefarious** misinformation to increase opposition to Catholic immigration from countries such as Ireland and Germany. The name came about because members, when asked about the party's activities, **dissembled** and said they "knew nothing." The party shortly died out, but modern candidates **exhume** parts of its platform from time to time, for example, calling for restrictions on liquor sales.

Teddy Roosevelt and the Bull Moose Party In 1912, former President Theodore Roosevelt tried to win back the presidency by challenging incumbent

FILLMORE
AND
DONELSON

THE UNION

FILLMORE & DONELSON

NATIONAL UNION.

"I know nothing but my Country, my whole Country, and nothing but my Country."

A campaign ribbon for the Know-Nothing party from 1856

Teddy Roosevelt's Bull Moose Party captured the imagination of the voting public in 1912.

William Howard Taft for the Republican nomination. Roosevelt lost, but a rolling stone gathers no moss, and he formed the Progressive Party, soon nicknamed the Bull Moose Party. This development split the Republican vote, and the Democrat, Woodrow Wilson, was elected President. Although Roosevelt, known for his colorful **verbiage** in speeches and **piquant** ideas, lost, much of his platform later became public policy.

Recent Third-Party Candidates

Some contenders, like H. Ross Perot in 1992 and 1996 and Ralph Nader in two of his bids—in 2000 and 2004—won enough votes to give **credence** to the idea of a third party in the United States. Some have viewed third-party candidates as "spoilers": They cannot win, but they'll siphon off enough votes to impact the election.

H. Ross Perot This billionaire businessman and folksy populist threw his hat into the presidential ring in 1992 as a Reform Party candidate. He received almost 20 million votes,

more than any other third-party candidate since Theodore Roosevelt in 1912.

Ralph Nader A trailblazing consumer advocate and four-time presidential candidate, Nader ran for president in 2000 on the Green Party ticket. Some Democrats feared he would draw votes from their candidate, Al Gore. Nader won just under three percent of the vote.

Legacy

The United States has the longest-surviving two-party system of any country. However, roughly one-third of voters today are not affiliated with either of the two major parties, and that number is growing. Many people are registering as Independents, which may signal an opportunity for the next third party.

Snap the code, or go to **vocabularyworkshop.com**

Definitions

Note the spelling, pronunciation, part(s) of speech, and definition(s) of each of the following words. Then write the word in the blank spaces in the illustrative sentence(s) following. Finally, study the lists of synonyms and antonyms.

1. cavort
(kə vôrt′)

(*v.*) to romp or prance around exuberantly; to make merry

The actors in the musical _____ on stage.

SYNONYM: gambol

2. credence
(krēd′ əns)

(*n.*) belief, mental acceptance

The government and the public failed to give _____ to the reports of an impending water shortage.

SYNONYMS: credit, trust, confidence
ANTONYMS: disbelief, skepticism, incredulity

3. decry
(di krī′)

(*v.*) to condemn, express strong disapproval; to officially depreciate

Every arm of government and every educational institution should _____ bigotry in all its forms.

SYNONYMS: denounce, censure, devalue
ANTONYMS: tout, commend, extol, laud, praise

4. dissemble
(di sem′ bəl)

(*v.*) to disguise or conceal, deliberately give a false impression

The young man was unable to _____ his feelings and admitted to having committed the crime.

SYNONYMS: dissimulate, mask, feign

5. distraught
(dis trôt′)

(*adj.*) very much agitated or upset as a result of emotion or mental conflict

The workforce became _____ in the wake of the 1929 stock market crash.

SYNONYM: distracted
ANTONYMS: calm, collected

6. eulogy
(yü′ lə jē)

(*n.*) a formal statement of commendation; high praise

The best friend and longtime law partner of the deceased delivered the _____ at the funeral.

SYNONYMS: panegyric, encomium, tribute
ANTONYMS: philippic, invective

7. evince
(i vins′)

(*v.*) to display clearly, to make evident, to provoke

The crowd did not _____ any signs of panic but moved in an orderly fashion to the nearest exits.

SYNONYMS: exhibit, manifest, occasion

8. exhume
(eks hyüm′)

(*v.*) to remove from a grave; to bring to light

Suspecting foul play, the coroner issued an order to _____ the body immediately.

SYNONYMS: disinter, unearth, uncover
ANTONYMS: bury, inter

9. feckless
(fek′ ləs)

(*adj.*) lacking in spirit and strength; ineffective, weak; irresponsible, unreliable

Although a _____ youth, he eventually matured into a hard-working and responsible citizen.

SYNONYMS: feeble, incompetent, ineffectual
ANTONYMS: competent, capable, effective

10. murky
(mər′ kē)

(*adj.*) dark and gloomy, obscure; lacking in clarity and precision

Many visitors have claimed to see a mysterious creature in the _____ waters of Loch Ness in Scotland.

SYNONYMS: dim, cloudy
ANTONYMS: clear, transparent, lucid, limpid

11. nefarious
(nə fâr′ ē əs)

(*adj.*) wicked, depraved, devoid of moral standards

Brutus and Cassius hatched a _____ plot to assassinate Julius Caesar on the steps of the Roman Senate.

SYNONYMS: iniquitous, reprehensible
ANTONYMS: virtuous, honorable, praiseworthy, meritorious

12. piquant
(pē′ kənt)

(*adj.*) stimulating to the taste or mind; spicy, pungent; appealingly provocative

The chef was an expert in making those _____ dishes that are characteristic of South Indian cooking.

SYNONYMS: zestful, tangy
ANTONYMS: bland, insipid, tasteless, mild

13. primordial
(prī môr′ dē əl)

(*adj.*) developed or created at the very beginning; going back to the most ancient times or earliest stage; fundamental, basic

The _____ stages of most civilizations are founded on common needs met by common goals.

SYNONYMS: original, primal

14. propinquity
(prō piŋ′ kwə tē)

(*n.*) nearness in place or time; kinship

The _____ of the two cities has created a greater metropolitan area that in effect is one city.

SYNONYM: similarity
ANTONYMS: remoteness, distance

15. substantive
(səb′ stən tiv)

(*adj.*) real, having a solid basis; considerable in number or amount; meaningful and on topic

The candidate dismissed the silly questions but took the time to answer the most _____ ones.

SYNONYMS: firm, substantial, meaty
ANTONYMS: imaginary, unreal, meaningless

16. unwonted
(un wōn′ tid)

(*adj.*) not usual or expected; not in character

The listless student answered with _____ spirit when the subject of military tactics was raised.

SYNONYMS: unusual, uncommon, unexpected, atypical
ANTONYMS: usual, customary, typical

17. utopian
(yü tō′ pē ən)

(*adj.*) founded upon or involving a visionary view of an ideal world; impractical

A number of American religious groups like the Shakers have built separate communities based on _____ schemes.

SYNONYM: idealistic
ANTONYMS: realistic, pragmatic

18. verbiage
(vər′ bē ij)

(*n.*) language that is too wordy or inflated in proportion to the sense or content, wordiness; a manner of expression

The contract was full of meaningless _____ that seemed designed to confuse the lay person.

SYNONYMS: prolixity, diction, jargon

19. verdant
(vər′ dənt)

(*adj.*) green in tint or color; immature in experience or judgment

The tourists on safari traveled over the _____ grasslands of Kenya in search of native wildlife.

SYNONYMS: artless, naïve
ANTONYMS: scorched, sere, barren

20. viscous
(vis′ kəs)

(*adj.*) having a gelatinous or gluey quality, lacking in easy movement or fluidity

The varnish left a _____ residue on the wood that was hard to remove.

SYNONYMS: sticky, thick
ANTONYMS: watery, aqueous

Choosing the Right Word

Select the **boldface** word that better completes each sentence. You might refer to the selection on pages 32–33 to see how most of these words are used in context.

1. The extraordinary musical talents of Wolfgang Amadeus Mozart (**evinced, dissembled**) themselves at an amazingly early age.

2. From the deck of our luxury liner, we occasionally caught sight of schools of porpoises (**cavorting, evincing**) playfully in the waves.

3. Far from being unpleasant, her slight foreign accent added an extra dash of spice to her already (**primordial, piquant**) personality.

4. The new mayor is a curious mixture of the hardheaded pragmatist and the (**utopian, murky**) reformer.

5. Not surprisingly, the address was a notably evenhanded affair in which the speaker cleverly mixed (**eulogy, verbiage**) with admonition.

Mozart composed his first minuet at the age of five.

6. When life was easy he was all dash and confidence, but in times of trouble his essentially (**piquant, feckless**) character came to the fore.

7. Unfortunately, the (**nefarious, verdant**) hopes and aspirations of my youth have been somewhat blighted by the icy blasts of reality.

8. Trying to read your (**viscous, utopian**) prose is just like trying to swim upstream through custard.

9. Because the playwright had hurried through her first draft, she had to make (**substantive, nefarious**) changes as she revised the dialogue.

10. His (**viscous, unwonted**) interest in the state of my finances strengthened my suspicions that he was about to ask for a loan.

11. The book has an interesting plot, but the author has practically smothered it in endless (**verbiage, eulogy**).

12. Despite all the reports of "miraculous" cures, you would be well advised to withhold (**verbiage, credence**) until the drug has been fully tested.

13. (**Exhumed, Distraught**) with grief, they sat motionless for hours, staring blankly into space.

14. An accomplished hypocrite usually finds it very easy to (**dissemble, decry**) his or her true feelings as circumstances dictate.

15. The behavior of armies in wartime often evinces the (**murky, primordial**) blood lust that civilized people have not yet fully overcome.

16. The United States is cooperating with the other nations of the world in an effort to check the (**feckless, nefarious**) trade in narcotics.

17. The (**credence, propinquity**) of our ideas on handling the problem made it very easy for my colleague and me to produce the report in record time.

18. The investigating committee (**decried, dissembled**) the use of substandard materials and slovenly workmanship in the housing project.

19. From the bridge, the rescue team could just make out the blurred image of a car beneath the (**murky, unwonted**) waters of the river.

20. Though the work hadn't seen the light of day for over a century, a daring impresario (**cavorted, exhumed**) and staged it to great public acclaim.

21. In my opinion, the columnist's observations about contemporary media and popular culture are humorous and wonderfully (**piquant, viscous**).

22. Members of Congress were relieved to learn that the current peace negotiations involve (**murky, substantive**) discussion of key issues.

23. Given my birthday's (**eulogy, propinquity**) to July 4th, my mother customarily decorates my wrapped gifts with red, white, and blue ribbons.

24. Plato's (**utopian, verdant**) description of the ideal society and its politics in *The Republic* exerted great influence on later philosophers like Aristotle.

25. The (**feckless, piquant**) efforts of our new quarterback caused the team to lose.

Synonyms

*Choose the word from this unit that is the same or most nearly the same in meaning as the **boldface** word or expression in the phrase. Write that word on the line. Use a dictionary if necessary.*

1. some **actual** doubt   _____

2. **primeval** history   _____

3. a **blossoming** garden   _____

4. delivered an emotional **testimonial**   _____

5. a slightly **gummy** coating of wax   _____

6. **played** in the wading pool   _____

7. feared for the **helpless** child   _____

8. an unwelcome **proximity**   _____

9. tried to calm the **frantic** parents   _____

10. could not make out the **unclear** image   _____

Antonyms

*Choose the word from this unit that is most nearly opposite in meaning to the **boldface** word or expression in the phrase. Write that word on the line. Use a dictionary if necessary.*

1. watered the **arid** lawn   _____

2. spent the summer **being serious**   _____

3. feeling **composed** after the accident   _____

4. make **minor** repairs   _____

5. published her lengthy **diatribe**   _____

Completing the Sentence

From the words in this unit, choose the one that best completes each of the following sentences. Write the word in the space provided.

1. An educated citizenry will not give __credence__ to wild charges of extremists seeking to undermine our political and economic system.

2. Although Aimée is usually quiet in class, her contribution to our political discussion yesterday was __substantive__.

3. The NCAA has in recent years cracked down hard on such __nefarious__ practices as "shaving points."

4. I have always regarded the man as something of a daredevil, but on this occasion he approached the problem with __unwonted__ caution.

5. In the hands of our hopelessly __feckless__ producer, what should have been a surefire hit turned into a resounding fiasco.

6. Even at an early age, my sister __evinced__ a strong interest in studying medicine.

7. Such spices as red pepper make many of the sauces used in Cajun cooking delightfully __piquant__.

8. Since my apartment is in such close __propinquity__ to my office, I usually walk to work.

9. For as far as the eye could see, __verdant__ fields of unripe corn swayed gently in the morning breeze.

10. How could we draw any clear ideas from a talk that was so disorganized, confused in language, and generally __murky__?

11. Sadly, the ___utopian___ schemes of high-minded idealists usually founder on the rocks of practical realities.

12. I believe there is an overall design to the universe that has been visible ever since the first thing crawled out of the ___primordial___ ooze.

13. When new evidence turned up in the case, the court ordered the coroner to ___exhume___ the victim's body and reexamine it.

14. Every Memorial Day, the mayor delivers a(n) ___eulogy___ extolling the selfless devotion of those who have died in defense of this country.

15. When news of the fire ran through town, ___distraught___ residents rushed to the scene of the blaze.

16. Though diesel fuels are not as thick as motor oil, they are a good deal more ___viscous___ than regular gasoline.

17. The new chairman ___decried___ what she called the "deplorable tendency of so many Americans to try to get something for nothing."

18. Though I prefer to be as open and aboveboard as possible, I have learned that it is sometimes wiser or more tactful to ___dissemble___.

19. He clothes his puny ideas in such highfalutin ___verbiage___ that they resemble gnats in top hats and tails.

20. When Bill was told that he had made the varsity wrestling team, he began to ___cavort___ around the gym like a young colt.

Writing: Words in Action

1. Look back at "Third Parties in American Politics" (pages 32–33), and think about the idea of a third party that focuses on a single issue. Suppose you are a third-party candidate running for president in the next election. What one issue would you want to focus on? Write a brief essay that explains your view of the issue and its importance to you and to the country in general. Use at least two details from the passage and three unit words to support your view.

2. Being the U.S. President is, arguably, one of the most challenging and powerful jobs in the world. Think of the range of particular qualities and skills someone needs to be an effective President. If you had to narrow those characteristics down to two, what would they be? Write at least three paragraphs explaining your answer. Support your ideas with specific details from your own experience and observations, as well as information you have gained from your reading, studies, or media viewing. Use three or more words from this unit in your answer.

Vocabulary in Context

Literary Text

The following excerpts are from Herman Melville's novel Moby-Dick. *Some of the words you have studied in this unit appear in **boldface** type. Complete each statement below the excerpt by circling the letter of the correct answer.*

1. Of all the pre-adamite whales yet **exhumed**, by far the largest is the Alabama one mentioned in the last chapter, and that was less than seventy feet in length in the skeleton.

   When something is **exhumed**, it is

   a. displayed in a museum
   b. removed from a grave
   c. examined by scientists
   d. documented by records

2. But even stripped of these supernatural surmisings, there was enough in the earthly make and incontestable character of the monster to strike the imagination with **unwonted** power.

   If something is **unwonted**, it is

   a. unusual
   b. frightening
   c. expected
   d. undesirable

3. It needs scarcely to be told, with what feelings, on the eve of a Nantucket voyage, I regarded those marble tablets, and by the **murky** light of that darkened, doleful day read the fate of the whalemen who had gone before me.

   Something that is **murky** is NOT

   a. dim
   b. cloudy
   c. gloomy
   d. clear

   Large sections of *Moby-Dick* focus on the American whaling industry in the nineteenth century.

4. Yet without power to kill, or change, or shun the fact; he likewise knew that to mankind he did now long **dissemble**; in some sort, did still. But that thing of his dissembling was only subject to his perceptibility, not to his will determinate.

   To **dissemble** is to

   a. disappoint
   b. inspire
   c. conceal
   d. deride

5. For as this appalling ocean surrounds the **verdant** land, so in the soul of man there lies one insular Tahiti, full of peace and joy, but encompassed by all the horrors of the half known life.

   Something **verdant** is

   a. barren
   b. green
   c. inhabited
   d. enduring

Interactive Quiz

Snap the code, or go to **vocabularyworkshop.com**

Vocabulary for Comprehension

*Read the following selection in which some of the words you have studied in Units 1–3 appear in **boldface** type. Then answer the questions on page 43.*

Although the Chicago fire caused enormous destruction, the city recovered quickly, as this passage shows.

(Line)

On the evening of October 8, 1871, at around 9 o'clock, the city of Chicago went up in flames. The exact **incendiary** agent remains
(5) unknown, but historians have **substantiated** the Chicago Fire Department's discovery that the blaze began in or near the barn of Mr. and Mrs. Patrick O'Leary, on the
(10) southwest side of the city. Official **credence**, however, has not been extended to the popular belief that it all started when the O'Learys' cow knocked over a lighted lantern.

(15) Whatever the initial spark, the city was a tinderbox. That summer had been unusually dry, and almost all the buildings, bridges, and even the sidewalks were made of wood.
(20) Construction over the previous years had proceeded rapidly and with little attention to fire safety. The **feckless** city council ignored all pleas to improve the level of fire protection,
(25) either by bolstering the fire department or by passing zoning laws. As a result of this inaction, the city of Chicago averaged about two fires a day.

(30) Driven by a strong wind out of the southwest, the October 8 fire was already out of control by the time the exhausted Chicago firefighters (who had been working the day before on
(35) another large fire) arrived. The wind carried the flames to the center of the city, where they consumed nearly every structure in their path. In a panic, the **distraught** population fled
(40) northward toward Lincoln Park and Lake Michigan. The fire raged for more than twenty-four hours until it rained on the morning of October 10.

In the days that followed,
(45) **reconnaissance** missions were conducted over the rubble that remained of homes, businesses, and tunnels. Three hundred were dead, nearly 100,000 were homeless, and
(50) property damage amounted to $200 million. Yet, four years later, Chicago was almost completely rebuilt. And today, the Chicago Fire Academy stands on the site of the O'Leary
(55) cowshed.

1. The primary purpose of the passage is to
   a. tell the story of the Chicago fire of 1871
   b. compare the Chicago fire with the San Francisco earthquake of 1906
   c. highlight the geography of Chicago
   d. focus on the heroism of the firefighters
   e. expose the incompetence of the city council

2. The meaning of **incendiary** (line 4) is
   a. criminal
   b. causative
   c. subversive
   d. inflammatory
   e. foreign

3. **Substantiated** (line 6) most nearly means
   a. disputed
   b. analyzed
   c. ignored
   d. verified
   e. dismissed

4. From the passage, it is clear that
   a. the fire started when the O'Learys' cow knocked over a lighted lantern
   b. no one really knows how or where the fire started
   c. the fire started in or near the O'Learys' barn
   d. the fire spread slowly but steadily
   e. Mr. and Mrs. O'Leary were responsible for setting the fire

5. **Credence** (line 11) is best defined as
   a. pardon
   b. acceptance
   c. condemnation
   d. mourning
   e. enthusiasm

6. Which of the following best describes the organizational structure of paragraph 2 (lines 15–28)?
   a. comparison and contrast
   b. spatial order
   c. cause and effect
   d. chronological order
   e. order of importance

7. The meaning of **feckless** (line 22) is
   a. corrupt
   b. effective
   c. popular
   d. conservative
   e. incompetent

8. From the passage, you can reasonably infer that all of the following played a role in the spread of the fire EXCEPT
   a. the fleeing population
   b. the minimal attention to safety in construction
   c. the exhaustion of the firefighters
   d. a strong wind
   e. the unusually dry summer

9. **Distraught** (line 39) is best defined as
   a. disheveled
   b. angry
   c. frantic
   d. bemused
   e. frightened

10. **Reconnaissance** (line 45) is best defined as
    a. detailed analysis
    b. calm evacuation
    c. scouting expedition
    d. slow deliberation
    e. court decision

11. The effect of the last sentence in the passage (lines 52–55) might best be described as
    a. fanciful
    b. melancholy
    c. ironic
    d. tragic
    e. farcical

12. Which of the following best describes the author's attitude toward the subject of the passage?
    a. disillusioned
    b. factual
    c. satiric
    d. skeptical
    e. enthusiastic

Two-Word Completions

Select the pair of words that best complete the meaning of each of the following passages.

1. Someone with a _____ nature is generally very good at _____, while more honest people give off unconscious cues that they are not telling the truth.
   a. distraught . . . emulating
   b. devious . . . dissembling
   c. ubiquitous . . . strategizing
   d. acquisitive . . . decrying

2. Despite the somewhat strident _____ of some professional critics and the inane _____ of a few literary pedants, the work enjoyed a notable popular success.
   a. encomiums . . . largesse
   b. verbiage . . . eulogies
   c. animadversions . . . carping
   d. gambits . . . sacrilege

3. For what must have been the first and only time in his life, the overly cautious general did not _____ or vacillate but committed his troops to battle with _____ celerity.
   a. arrogate . . . overt
   b. temporize . . . unwonted
   c. carp . . . myopic
   d. dissemble . . . feckless

4. From the top of the mountain that summer afternoon, I looked out on a(n) _____ panorama of fields and pasturelands through which countless streams and rivulets _____ like so many serpents slithering lazily across a carpet.
   a. substantive . . . exhumed
   b. avid . . . congealed
   c. verdant . . . undulated
   d. primordial . . . cavorted

5. Someone who is by nature as skeptical as I am usually refuses to give any _____ to the kinds of wild allegations thrown about in an election until they have been _____ by solid evidence.
   a. credence . . . substantiated
   b. celerity . . . decried
   c. largesse . . . exhumed
   d. propriety . . . eschewed

6. Little did we realize, as we _____ blithely on the beach during those _____ and cloudless days of spring 1914, that the world was moving inexorably into the maelstrom of total war.
   a. evinced . . . piquant
   b. belabored . . . utopian
   c. emulated . . . insatiable
   d. cavorted . . . halcyon

7. The senator hoped his colleagues would find his _____ argument about the deficit to be _____ .
   a. histrionic . . . invidious
   b. germane . . . murky
   c. coherent . . . tenable
   d. viscous . . . nefarious

Idioms

In one of the letters about women's suffrage (see pages 12–13), the writer predicts that after Wyoming's decision to allow women to vote, other Western states and territories will "follow suit."

"Follow suit" is an idiom. An **idiom** is a group of words whose meaning is different from the literal meanings of each word considered individually. For example, "follow suit" means "do the same as has been done previously." Speakers and writers often use idioms to add interest and an air of informality to their style and tone. While it is sometimes possible to determine the meaning of an idiom from its context, you should memorize the meanings of common idioms. For others, you may need to consult a dictionary.

Choosing the Right Idiom

Read each sentence. Use context clues to figure out the meaning of each idiom in **boldface** *print. Then write the letter of the definition for the idiom in the sentence.*

1. To her older colleagues, the new personal trainer seemed **wet behind the ears** on her first day. _____

2. After tiring in the first half of the race, Bryan and Phil got a **second wind** in the last few laps. _____

3. I was **fit to be tied** when the airline lost my suitcases. _____

4. Any library **worth its salt** has a variety of both print and digital encyclopedias. _____

5. Because the Smiths suspected that the rental contract was not **on the up and up,** they refused to sign it. _____

6. One recently hired employee left the engineering department last week for **greener pastures.** _____

7. Although we read the directions twice, we couldn't **make heads or tails of** them. _____

8. The homeowners and the real estate agent tried to remain polite, but they were clearly **at odds**. _____

9. The bride hoped that **down the line** the groom would begin helping her address the wedding invitations. _____

10. Although I once doubted I would make the varsity team, now I believe it is **in the cards.** _____

a. furious

b. in the future

c. likely to happen

d. a better situation

e. renewed energy

f. in disagreement

g. understand

h. inexperienced and young

i. legal

j. deserving of respect

Writing with Idioms

Find the meaning of each idiom. (Use an online or print dictionary if necessary.) Then write a sentence for each idiom.

1. done in

_____

2. gain ground

_____

3. by the book

_____

4. a full plate

_____

5. set up shop

_____

_____

6. in a nutshell

_____

_____

7. sound bite

_____

_____

8. ax to grind

_____

9. bite the bullet

_____

10. par for the course

_____

11. get wind of

_____

12. with bated breath

_____

Denotation and Connotation

The literal meaning of a word is its **denotation**, or the definition of the word found in a dictionary. In contrast, a word's **connotation** is its implied meaning. Many words have connotations that are either *positive* or *negative*.

For example, a writer could describe one character looking at another as *watching, staring, gazing, leering, scrutinizing, ogling,* and so on. Each of these different words conveys a different set of associations or images in a reader's mind. Writers choose the particular word that will help them best communicate a precise mood or message.

Consider these synonyms for the word *utopian:*

idealistic   sublime   quixotic   illusory

Idealistic and *sublime* have positive connotations, suggesting noble-minded or lofty ideas, values, and behaviors. *Quixotic* and *illusory* have negative connotations, suggesting foolish impracticality or deception.

> **Think:** Residents would welcome an idealistic or sublime vision of community reform but would criticize or reject calls for quixotic or illusory changes.

Look at these examples of words that are similar in denotation but have different connotations.

NEUTRAL	POSITIVE	NEGATIVE
dwell on	emphasize	belabor
avid	enthusiastic	coveting
unwonted	extraordinary	aberrant

Skilled writers and readers need to understand the emotional power that certain words have and pay attention to the differing nuances of words with similar denotations.

Shades of Meaning

Write a plus sign (+) in the box if the word has a positive connotation.
Write a minus sign (–) if the word has a negative connotation. Put a zero (0)
if the word is neutral.

1. decry ☐   **2.** congeal ☐   **3.** propinquity ☐   **4.** distraught ☐

5. murky ☐   **6.** germane ☐   **7.** brackish ☐   **8.** animadversion ☐

9. accost ☐   **10.** devious ☐   **11.** eulogy ☐   **12.** coherent ☐

13. overt ☐   **14.** sacrilege ☐   **15.** undulate ☐   **16.** pejorative ☐

Expressing the Connotation

Read each sentence. Select the word in parentheses that expresses the connotation (positive, negative, or neutral) given at the beginning of the sentence.

negative   **1.** I have enjoyed several of the author's previous novels, but the (**diction, verbiage**) used throughout this one made reading it tedious.

negative   **2.** With one rap of his gavel, the judge (**rudely, summarily**) ordered the defense attorneys to leave his chambers.

positive   **3.** Featuring a variety of (**piquant, suitable**) seafood salads, the buffet was well worth the cost.

negative   **4.** The ineffective advertisement relied on (**common, banal**) descriptive phrases and images.

positive   **5.** We had tears in our eyes after hearing the (**encomium, sermon**) to the injured firefighters.

neutral   **6.** During the play's final act, the tearful heroine questions her sister's (**dubious, nefarious**) behavior.

neutral   **7.** Predictably, the newspaper's (**unfortunate, invidious**) headline stirred up controversy in the community.

positive   **8.** With a stunning view of the castle and elegant decor, the hotel room offered a(n) (**halcyon, agreeable**) atmosphere.

Challenge: Using Connotation

Choose vocabulary words from Units 1–3 to replace the highlighted words in the sentences below. Then explain how the connotation of the replacement word changes the tone of the sentence.

largesse	histrionic	acquisitive
talisman	carping	suppliant

1. Hearing his unexpectedly **critical** _____ comments changed the team's opinion of their new coach.

_____

_____

2. The film review emphasized the **dramatic** _____ manner in which the lead actor delivered his lines in the final scene.

_____

_____

3. The minister remarked on the surprising **gift** _____ to the church building fund given by an anonymous donor.

_____

_____

Classical Roots

cred—to believe

The root *cred* appears in **credence** (page 34). The literal meaning is "belief," but the word now suggests a belief that is accepted. Some other words based on the same root are listed below.

accreditation	credibility	creditor	credulity
credentials	creditable	credo	credulous

From the list of words above, choose the one that corresponds to each of the brief definitions below. Write the word in the blank space in the illustrative sentence below the definition. Use an online or print dictionary if necessary.

1. a person or an organization to which money is owed

The bank denied her request for a loan when they saw that she had made late payments to a past _____.

2. an undue readiness to believe; a lack of critical judgment

The wily con artists exploited their victim's _____.

3. a statement or summary of faith or fundamental belief; an authoritative statement of religious belief *("I believe")*

The _____ of our hiking club is "Take only pictures; leave only footprints."

4. inclined to believe very readily, gullible

The naïve young man seemed as _____ as a child.

5. official authorization or approval (often used in regard to academic affairs)

The college received _____ as an institution of higher learning.

6. bringing or deserving credit or honor

Despite limited rehearsal time, the cast did a(n) _____ job on that play.

7. references, testimonials, or other (usually written) evidence of identity or status ("that which provides a basis for belief")

The security guard demanded to see their _____ before they could enter the building.

8. worthiness of belief

At the hearing, a panel of experts questioned the _____ of the advertisement.

*Read the following selection, taking note of the **boldface** words and their contexts. These words are among those you will be studying in Unit 4. As you complete the exercises in this unit, it may help to refer to the way the words are used below.*

Reforming the Security Council
<Newspaper Editorial>

For more than a decade, diplomats and politicians the world over have sought to reform the United Nations Security Council. While everyone seems to agree that reform could increase the Council's effectiveness, there is less **concord** as to how to bring it about. Many nations favor changes that suit their own interests and **grouse** about their rivals' points of view. As the debate drags on, proposals for reform pile up like **flotsam** on the shore, each idea thwarted by a barrage of **mordant** objections. So the process of reform has proven less efficient than the Security Council itself, and hope for change threatens to **atrophy**.

The Security Council was created to serve as a **bastion** of peace and security in the world. It has the power to mediate disputes and to authorize peacekeeping operations, sanctions, and military action.

Its members include representatives from fifteen nations, five of which hold permanent seats. A minimum of nine votes is required for the Council to pass a resolution, but the five permanent members have the lion's share of influence over important decisions. If any permanent member votes against a proposed measure, the resolution does not pass.

This veto power held by the permanent members is the chief source of the Council's inefficacy. When there is disagreement among permanent members, a single "no" vote is enough to prevent the Council from taking action. Just the threat of a veto can throw negotiations into **disarray**, holding the Council hostage to the slow workings of diplomacy. This cumbersome process prevents the Council from reacting quickly to the **exigencies** of political crises. Accordingly, many critics

The UN building in New York City, as seen from the East River

A meeting of the UN Security Council

claim it is **incumbent** upon reformers to amend the Council's voting procedures. Others demand that the number of non-permanent members be increased to limit the permanent members' power. While there is wisdom in both of these suggestions, debate as to how the U.N. can implement such measures remains **frenetic**, with no end to the **stratagems** by which each nation hopes to gain advantage.

An increasing number of critics have suggested doing away with permanent membership entirely and making all members of the Council temporary officials. While proponents of this reform may **glean** support from some corners, there is little chance of its coming to pass. The permanent members will not willingly give up their privileged positions: Since they have the power to veto the proposal, it is **ludicrous** to expect that such a resolution could ever be enacted. Moreover, permanent membership is designed to reflect the realities of global politics. In theory, permanent members consist of the nations that contribute the most

pecuniary and military support to the U.N. and that have the greatest power to influence world affairs by diplomatic, economic, or other means.

That is not necessarily the case today. The list of permanent members was drawn up just after World War II and no longer reflects the balance of global power. The fortunes of many nations have changed, for better or worse, in the past six decades. To better reflect today's world, influential nations such as Germany and Japan should be made permanent members, along with emerging regional powers like India, South Africa, and Brazil. And the Council's voting process must be improved. Achieving these aims will require an unusual degree of compromise and **consummate** diplomatic tact, and there is no doubt that some nations will be **nettled** by the result. But the only alternative is to allow the Council to remain an ineffective institution—and this is an outcome that benefits no one.

Snap the code, or go to
vocabularyworkshop.com

A UN peacekeeper monitors the border between Israel and Lebanon.

Definitions

Note the spelling, pronunciation, part(s) of speech, and definition(s) of each of the following words. Then write the word in the blank spaces in the illustrative sentence(s) following. Finally, study the lists of synonyms and antonyms.

1. atrophy
(a' trə fē)

(*n.*) the wasting away of a body organ or tissue; any progressive decline or failure; (*v.*) to waste away

The _____ of the downtown business district began when two huge malls opened.

The patient's muscles have _____.

SYNONYMS: (*n.*) degeneration, deterioration; (*v.*) wither
ANTONYMS: (*n.*) growth; (*v.*) mature

2. bastion
(bas' chən)

(*n.*) a fortified place, stronghold

Contrary to popular belief, the military is not always a _____ of political conservatism.

SYNONYMS: citadel, rampart, parapet

3. concord
(kän' kôrd)

(*n.*) a state of agreement, harmony, unanimity; a treaty, pact, covenant

A spirit of _____ was restored when the company compensated its employees.

ANTONYMS: disagreement, strife, discord

4. consummate
(*v.*, kän' sə māt;
adj., kən' sə mət)

(*adj.*) complete or perfect in the highest degree; (*v.*) to bring to a state of completion or perfection

Michelangelo's paintings on the ceiling of the Sistine Chapel in the Vatican are works of _____ artistry.

The lawyers could not _____ the settlement until the two parties met face to face.

SYNONYMS: (*adj.*) masterful; (*v.*) clinch, conclude
ANTONYMS: (*v.*) launch, initiate, begin, kick off

5. disarray
(dis ə rā')

(*n.*) disorder, confusion; (*v.*) to throw into disorder

The burgled home was in a state of _____.

If you leave the window open, a breeze may _____ the papers on the desktop.

SYNONYMS: (*n.*) disorganization; (*v.*) dishevel, mess up
ANTONYMS: (*n.*) organization, order, tidiness

6. exigency
(ek' sə jən sē)

(*n.*, often *pl.*) urgency, pressure; urgent demand, pressing need; an emergency

He emphasized the _____ of the situation by requesting the immediate dispatch of rescue teams.

SYNONYMS: requirement, crisis

7. flotsam
(flät′ səm)

(*n.*) floating debris; homeless, impoverished people
After the two ships collided, the survivors clung to various pieces of _____ and hoped for rescue.
SYNONYM: floating wreckage

8. frenetic
(frə net′ ik)

(*adj.*) frenzied, highly agitated
When a court order was issued, the social services department made a _____ search for the missing report.
SYNONYMS: frantic, overwrought
ANTONYMS: calm, controlled, relaxed, leisurely

9. glean
(glēn)

(*v.*) to gather bit by bit; to gather small quantities of grain left in a field by the reapers
By means of painstaking investigation, the detectives will eventually _____ the truth.
SYNONYMS: cull, pick up

10. grouse
(graús)

(*n.*) a type of game bird; a complaint; (*v.*) to complain, grumble
The patient's latest _____ was that he did not get any dessert with his dinner the night before.
Those who just stand around and _____ about their low salaries are not likely to get raises.
SYNONYMS: (*v.*) kvetch, bellyache

11. incarcerate
(in kär′ sə rāt)

(*v.*) to imprison, confine, jail
They will _____ the convicted felon at the state penitentiary.
SYNONYM: intern; ANTONYMS: liberate, free

12. incumbent
(in kəm′ bənt)

(*adj.*) obligatory, required; (*n.*) one who holds a specific office at the time spoken of
Voting on election day is a duty _____ on all Americans who value a democratic government.
The _____ has the advantage when standing for reelection but does not have a guarantee of victory.
SYNONYMS: (*adj.*) mandatory, necessary
ANTONYMS: (*adj.*) optional, unnecessary

13. jocular
(jäk′ yə lər)

(*adj.*) humorous, jesting, jolly, joking
After receiving the news that she was ahead in the polls, the candidate was in a delightfully _____ mood.
SYNONYMS: waggish, facetious, droll
ANTONYMS: solemn, grave, earnest, grim

14. ludicrous
(lüd' ə krəs)

(*adj.*) ridiculous, laughable, absurd

Her comment was so _____ that we finally understood that she was joking.

SYNONYMS: risible, preposterous
ANTONYMS: heartrending, poignant, pathetic

15. mordant
(môr' dənt)

(*adj.*) biting or caustic in thought, manner, or style; sharply or bitterly harsh

The actor was upset by the _____ criticism of the gossip columnist who seemed out to ruin his reputation.

SYNONYMS: acrimonious, acidulous, sardonic, scathing
ANTONYMS: bland, mild, gentle, soothing

16. nettle
(net' əl)

(*n.*) a prickly or stinging plant; (*v.*) to arouse displeasure, impatience, or anger; to vex or irritate severely

If you are pricked by a _____, aloe cream will soothe and reduce the sting.

The principal was _____ by the student's disrespectful behavior.

SYNONYMS: (*v.*) peeve, annoy, incense, gall
ANTONYMS: (*v.*) please, delight, soothe, pacify

17. pecuniary
(pi kyü' nē er ē)

(*adj.*) consisting of or measured in money; of or related to money

The couple was forced by _____ considerations to sell their large home and buy a smaller one.

SYNONYM: monetary

18. pusillanimous
(pyü sə lan' ə məs)

(*adj.*) contemptibly cowardly or mean-spirited

It is often said that bullies, when tested, are the most _____ people of all.

SYNONYM: lily-livered
ANTONYMS: stouthearted, courageous

19. recumbent
(ri kəm' bənt)

(*adj.*) in a reclining position, lying down, in the posture of one sleeping or resting

The tired toddlers were _____ on the couch after playing all afternoon in the yard.

SYNONYMS: prone, supine, inactive
ANTONYMS: erect, energetic, dynamic

20. stratagem
(strat' ə jəm)

(*n.*) a scheme to outwit or deceive an opponent or to gain an end

The defense attorney used a clever _____ to curry sympathy for her client.

SYNONYMS: trick, ploy, subterfuge

Choosing the Right Word

*Select the **boldface** word that better completes each sentence. You might refer to the selection on pages 50–51 to see how most of these words are used in context.*

Victorian dress with a high neckline and long, full skirt

1. In Victorian times, fashionable ladies (**disarrayed, incarcerated**) their waists in tight corsets to achieve a chic "hourglass" figure.

2. During the 19th century, it was fashionable to spend a few weeks in the fall hunting (**grouse, nettles**), pheasants, and other game birds.

3. Comfortably (**recumbent, frenetic**) in the shade of the elm tree, I watched the members of the football team go through a long, hard workout.

4. The affairs of our city are in such (**disarray, flotsam**) that the state may have to intervene to restore some semblance of order.

5. Before the ceremony began, we all bowed our heads and hoped for unity, peace, and (**concord, atrophy**) among all nations.

6. We were fascinated by the (**mordant, frenetic**) scene on the floor of the stock exchange as brokers struggled to keep up with sudden price changes.

7. I have always regarded our schools and colleges as citadels of learning and (**bastions, stratagems**) against ignorance and superstition.

8. Do you really think that those (**jocular, recumbent**) remarks are appropriate on such a solemn occasion?

9. In the shelter, I saw for the first time people who'd been beaten and discouraged by life—the so-called derelicts and (**flotsam, incumbents**) of the great city.

10. The only way we'll really be able to increase productivity is to offer our employees a few solid (**frenetic, pecuniary**) incentives to work harder.

11. We were able to (**consummate, glean**) only a few shreds of useful information from his long, pretentious speech.

12. Of the ten Congressional seats in our state, only one was won by a new member; all the other winners were (**incumbents, bastions**).

13. There are few things in life as (**frenetic, ludicrous**) as an unqualified person trying to assume the trappings of authority.

14. The huge influx of wealth that resulted from foreign conquests led in part to the physical and moral (**atrophy, flotsam**) of the Roman ruling class.

15. What we need to cope with this crisis is not cute (**grouses, stratagems**) but a bold, realistic plan and the courage to carry it out.

16. All that I needed to (**consummate, nettle**) the most important deal of my career was her signature on the dotted line.

17. To feel fear in difficult situations is natural, but to allow one's conduct to be governed by fear is (**jocular, pusillanimous**).

18. I noticed with approval that his (**pecuniary, mordant**) remarks were intended to deflate the pompous and unmask the hypocritical.

19. It has been said that the only way to handle a (**nettle, stratagem**), or any difficult problem, without being stung is to grasp it firmly and decisively.

20. A born leader is someone who can rise to the (**incumbents, exigencies**) of any crisis that he or she may be confronted with.

21. Why did my grandparents feel it necessary to show the (**pecuniary, ludicrous**) photo of me dressed as a chicken to my new girlfriend?

22. Although most of the diners' comments were favorable, several (**grouses, concords**) about the soggy salads dismayed the chef.

23. Recent polls confirm a widespread (**atrophy, nettle**) in small business owners' abilities to secure bank loans at reasonable rates.

24. In his 1907 painting *The Sick Child*, Edvard Munch's depiction of a (**jocular, recumbent**) adolescent creates a mood of despair.

25. The undisciplined puppy (**disarrayed, consummated**) the boxes in the garage.

Synonyms

*Choose the word from this unit that is the same or most nearly the same in meaning as the **boldface** word or expression in the phrase. Write that word on the line. Use a dictionary if necessary.*

1. gripes about every change in the routine   _____

2. received **financial** compensation   _____

3. the ill-conceived **ruse**   _____

4. collected tidbits of information   _____

5. a longtime **bulwark** of resistance   _____

6. prostrate on a hospital bed   _____

7. craven behavior   _____

8. a **witty** conversation   _____

9. immured for years in a dank dungeon   _____

10. irks her coworkers with senseless chatter   _____

Antonyms

*Choose the word from this unit that is most nearly opposite in meaning to the **boldface** word or expression in the phrase. Write that word on the line. Use a dictionary if necessary.*

1. made a **daring** attempt _____

2. enthusiasm that **developed** _____

3. stayed **upright** without moving _____

4. **release** the trapped bat _____

5. a **humorless** manner _____

Completing the Sentence

From the words in this unit, choose the one that best completes each of the following sentences. Write the word in the space provided.

1. The defeated army fled in such ___disarray___ that before long it had become little more than a uniformed mob.

2. People who are used to the unhurried atmosphere of a country town often find it hard to cope with the ___frenetic___ pace of big-city life.

3. Almost every case of muscle or tissue ___atrophy___ is the result of disease, prolonged disuse, or changes in cell nutrition.

4. I have yet to meet an adult who did not ___nettle grouse___ about the taxes he or she had to pay.

5. I get my best ideas while lying down; the ___recumbent___ position seems to stimulate my brain.

6. The ___exigency___ of my present financial situation demand that I curtail all unnecessary expenses for at least a month.

7. Even critics of our penal system admit that as long as hardened criminals are ___incarcerated___, they can't commit further crimes.

8. Shakespeare's Timon of Athens is a disillusioned misanthrope who spends his time hurling ___mordant___ barbs at the rest of mankind.

9. As soon as he struck the opening chords of the selection, we realized that we were listening to a(n) ___consummate___ master of the piano.

10. The ___flotsam___ that we observed here and there in the harbor bore mute testimony to the destructive power of the storm.

11. I regret that Nancy was ___nettled___ by my unfavorable review of her short story, but I had to express my opinion honestly.

12. Most people regarded the government's attempt to avert a war by buying off the aggressor as not only shameful but ___pusillanimous___.

13. It was pleasant to see the usually quiet and restrained Mr. Baxter in such a(n) ___jocular___ and expansive mood.

14. It is ___incumbent___ on all of us to do whatever we can to help our community overcome this crisis.

15. Since I had had only one year of high-school French, my attempts to speak that language on my trip to Paris were pretty ___ludicrous___.

16. Peace is not just the absence of war but a positive state of ___concord___ among the nations of the world.

17. Despite all their highfalutin malarkey about helping the poor, I suspect that their interest in the project is purely ___pecuniary___.

18. Though next to nothing is known about Homer, historians have been able to ___glean___ a few odd facts about him from studying his works.

19. The high ground east of the river formed a natural ___bastion___, which we decided to defend with all the forces at our disposal.

20. The purpose of our ___stratagem___ was to draw in the safety so that Tom could get behind him to receive a long pass.

Writing: Words in Action

1. Look back at "Reforming the Security Council" (pages 50–51). Think about how the U.N. Security Council could become more effective. Which one of the possible changes to the Council that the author mentions do you think makes the most sense? Write a persuasive essay explaining the single most important change to the Security Council that you would like to see made. Use at least two details from the passage and three unit words to support your argument.

2. *"Nearly all men can stand adversity, but if you want to test a man's character, give him power."—Abraham Lincoln*

Do you agree with Lincoln's statement? How does having power bring out the best or the worst in a person? Write an essay that explains your opinion, using specific examples from your reading (refer to pages 50–51), your studies, or your own experience and observations to clarify and support your ideas. Write at least three paragraphs, and use three or more words from this unit.

Vocabulary in Context

The following excerpts are from Thomas Hardy's novels Jude the Obscure *and* Tess of the d'Urbervilles. *Some of the words you have studied in this unit appear in* **boldface** *type. Complete each statement below the excerpt by circling the letter of the correct answer.*

1. The sight of it [a milestone], unimpaired, within its screen of grass and **nettles**, lit in his soul a spark of the old fire. Surely his plan should be to move onward through good and ill—to avoid morbid sorrow even though he did see uglinesses in the world? (*Jude the Obscure*)

    Nettles are
    a. tiny pebbles   **c.** prickly plants
    b. thick roots   **d.** crumbling rocks

2. As a set-off against such discussions as these there had come an improvement in their **pecuniary** position, which earlier in their experience would have made them cheerful. (*Jude the Obscure*)

    A **pecuniary** position is related to
    a. money   **c.** family
    b. emotions   **d.** taxes

3. To have suggested such a story was certainly not very exhilarating, in a serious view of their position. However, in a few minutes Sue seemed to see that their position this morning had a **ludicrous** side, and wiping her eyes she laughed. (*Jude the Obscure*)

    Something **ludicrous** is
    a. pathetic   **c.** fleeting
    b. arbitrary   **d.** absurd

The 1998 TV version of *Tess of the d'Urbervilles* stars Justine Waddell.

4. She musingly turned to withdraw, passing near an altar-tomb, the oldest of them all, on which was a **recumbent** figure. In the dusk she had not noticed it before, and would hardly have noticed it now but for an odd fancy that the effigy moved. (*Tess of the d'Urbervilles*)

    Someone who is **recumbent** is NOT
    a. talkative   **c.** sturdy
    b. hideous   **d.** standing

5. They [the mountain summits] had a low and unassuming aspect from this upland, though as approached on the other side from Blackmoor in her childhood they were as lofty **bastions** against the sky. (*Tess of the d'Urbervilles*)

    Bastions are
    a. strongholds   **c.** shadows
    b. benedictions   **d.** omens

Interactive Quiz

Snap the code, or go to **vocabularyworkshop.com**

*Read the following selection, taking note of the **boldface** words and their contexts. These words are among those you will be studying in Unit 5. As you complete the exercises in this unit, it may help to refer to the way the words are used below.*

What Is Pop Art?

<Essay>

Roy Lichtenstein's "In the Car," 1963, looks like a comic strip but measures more than 6 feet wide.

What is pop art? The simple answer: Art based on popular culture. Beginning in the mid-1950s and continuing for more than a decade, pop artists borrowed images directly from everyday popular culture. Drawing upon this seemingly **mundane** content, pop artists created bold, overpowering images. With great **acuity**, their canvases detailed such familiar things as comic strips, American flags, race cars, popular movie stars, and even boxes of laundry detergent.

In many ways, pop art was a reaction to abstract expressionism, the dominant style of painting during the 1940s and 1950s. Abstract expressionist paintings were nonrepresentational; they did not **delineate** objects directly. Instead, artists used abstract shapes and **nuances** in color to express personal ideas and feelings. Pop artists viewed abstract expressionism as elitist—too **esoteric** to be appreciated by most museum goers. In response, they returned to representational art. This was a time when consumerism was booming in the United States and advertising had become **ubiquitous**. So the world around the pop artists became a **fecund** source of images.

At first, pop art **garnered** much negative criticism. Some critics complained that pop art's **penchant** for reproducing existing images—such as painting a portrait of a can of soup—was too easy. Others claimed the pop artist's love of commercial images **enervated** traditional artistic values. A few critics even implied that pop art was **depraved**, or at least was

Warhol, Andy (1928–1987). *Vegetarian Vegetable from Campbell's Soup II.* 1969. Screenprint, $35\frac{1}{8}$ x $23\frac{1}{16}$ in. Gift of Mr. and Mrs. Peter Eider-Orley, 1972 (1972.724.3). The Metropolitan Museum of Art, New York, NY.

devoid of aesthetic principles. Pop artists dismissed these arguments as so much **sophistry**. Why should traditional art be **hallowed** and commercial art be dismissed as vulgar? Was it a declaration of truth or a mere **fiat** when a critic pronounced one piece art and another trash?

No doubt reminding themselves that beauty is in the eye of the beholder, pop artists ignored the critics and continued to explore the relationship between the two types of art, playing around with commercial images and presenting them as works of art. Roy Lichtenstein, for example, chose comic strips as his main subject. Reproducing all the **idiosyncrasies** of this format, including voice balloons and printing dots, he chose frames that showed violent action or sentimental romance. The images, enlarged to monumental size and completely out of context, took on a new significance.

Andy Warhol is **reputed** to have eaten soup for lunch every day for twenty years. Perhaps that explains why he, the best-known of the pop artists, first became famous for his images of soup cans and other consumer products. Later, glamour and fame became a central theme of his work, and he produced **sumptuous** silkscreens of celebrities, such as Marilyn Monroe and Elvis Presley. Thanks to an **overweening** desire for publicity, Andy Warhol helped make pop art a household term, and he became one of the wealthiest artists of all time.

Pop art sculptors were also active, again taking consumer products as their starting point. Claes Oldenburg stuffed and painted cloth to produce giant hamburgers, toothpaste tubes, and ice cream bars. Like so much pop art, Oldenburg's "soft sculptures" remind us that, in pop art, the ordinary things of life become strange and things that we take for granted are seen anew, as if for the first time.

Pop art outlived its critics, and today, a half century later, its seriousness is not in doubt. As a movement, pop art ended, but not before greatly expanding the range of subjects, attitudes, and techniques available to all artists. Thanks to the pop artists, younger generations of painters, sculptors, and photographers now explore the world in more imaginative and thought-provoking ways.

Snap the code, or go to **vocabularyworkshop.com**

Definitions

Note the spelling, pronunciation, part(s) of speech, and definition(s) of each of the following words. Then write the word in the blank spaces in the illustrative sentence(s) following. Finally, study the lists of synonyms and antonyms.

1. acuity
(ə kyü′ ə tē)

(*n.*) sharpness (particularly of the mind or senses)

The _____ of most people's hearing diminishes as they grow older.

SYNONYM: acuteness
ANTONYMS: dullness, obtuseness

2. delineate
(di lin′ ē āt)

(*v.*) to portray, sketch, or describe in accurate and vivid detail; to represent pictorially

The architects will _____ the main features of their plan at the next client meeting.

SYNONYMS: picture, render

3. depraved
(di prāvd′)

(*adj.*) marked by evil and corruption, devoid of moral principles

Oscar Wilde's novel *The Picture of Dorian Gray* is about a _____ man whose portrait reveals his wickedness.

SYNONYMS: perverted, degenerate, vicious, corrupt
ANTONYMS: moral, virtuous, upright, uncorrupted

4. enervate
(en′ ər vāt)

(*v.*) to weaken or lessen the mental, moral, or physical vigor of; enfeeble, hamstring

Unfortunately, the great musician's mind was _____ by disease in the last decade of her life.

SYNONYMS: impair, cripple, paralyze
ANTONYMS: invigorate, strengthen, buttress

5. esoteric
(es ə ter′ ik)

(*adj.*) intended for or understood by only a select few, private, secret

The fraternity developed a set of _____ rites that had to be performed by anyone seeking membership.

SYNONYMS: cryptic, arcane, recondite
ANTONYMS: accessible, comprehensible, intelligible

6. fecund
(fek′ und)

(*adj.*) fruitful in offspring or vegetation; intellectually productive

The remarkably _____ mind of Albert Einstein produced theories that revolutionized the science of physics.

SYNONYMS: fertile, teeming, prolific
ANTONYMS: infertile, barren, unproductive

7. fiat
(fē ət)

(*n.*) an arbitrary order or decree; a command or act of will or consciousness

The ruler instituted several new _____.

SYNONYMS: dictum, ukase

8. figment
(fig′ mənt)

(*n.*) a fabrication of the mind; an arbitrary notion

The silhouette of a man on the porch was a mere _____ of your overheated imagination.

SYNONYMS: invention, fancy

9. garner
(gär′ nər)

(*v.*) to acquire as the result of effort; to gather and store away, as for future use

Over the years, the writer was able to _____ some wisdom that she passed on to others in her books.

SYNONYMS: collect, accumulate, accrue
ANTONYMS: scatter, squander, waste, dissipate

10. hallow
(hal′ ō)

(*v.*) to set apart as holy or sacred, sanctify, consecrate; to honor greatly, revere

In the Gettysburg Address, Lincoln _____ the battlefield on which the Union soldiers fought and died.

SYNONYMS: venerate, bless
ANTONYMS: defile, profane

11. idiosyncrasy
(id ē ə siŋ′ krə sē)

(*n.*) a peculiarity that serves to distinguish or identify

The fact that the plurals of some nouns are formed irregularly is an _____ of English grammar.

SYNONYMS: quirk, mannerism

12. ignominy
(ig′ nə min ē)

(*n.*) shame and disgrace

He went from glory to _____.

SYNONYMS: humiliation, disrepute, odium
ANTONYMS: honor, acclaim

13. mundane
(mən dān′)

(*adj.*) earthly, worldly, relating to practical and material affairs; concerned with what is ordinary

The painter left all _____ concerns to her sister while she single-mindedly pursued her artistic goals.

SYNONYMS: prosaic, humdrum, routine, sublunary
ANTONYMS: heavenly, spiritual, transcendental

14. nuance
(nü' äns)

(*n.*) a subtle or slight variation (as in color, meaning, quality), delicate gradation or shade of difference

In his writing, the poet paid close attention to every _____ of meaning in the words he chose.

SYNONYMS: shade, nicety, refinement

15. overweening
(ō vər wē 'niŋ)

(*adj.*) conceited, presumptuous; excessive, immoderate

It was the _____ confidence of the candidate that prevented her from acknowledging her weaknesses.

SYNONYMS: arrogant, unbridled, inflated
ANTONYMS: restrained, understated, meek

16. penchant
(pen' chənt)

(*n.*) a strong attraction or inclination

A teacher with a _____ for belaboring the obvious is bound to be boring.

SYNONYMS: proclivity, predilection
ANTONYMS: disinclination, aversion

17. reputed
(ri pyüt' id)

(*adj.*) according to reputation or general belief; having widespread acceptance and good reputation; (*part.*) alleged

Although he is the _____ head of a crime syndicate, he has never spent time in jail.

SYNONYMS: putative, reputable
ANTONYMS: proven, corroborated, authenticated

18. sophistry
(säf' ə strē)

(*n.*) reasoning that seems plausible but is actually unsound; a fallacy

The couple was beguiled into buying a bigger house than they needed by the clever _____ of the broker.

SYNONYM: specious reasoning

19. sumptuous
(səmp' chü əs)

(*adj.*) costly, rich, magnificent

The _____ feast honoring the king's birthday was followed by musical entertainment.

SYNONYMS: lavish, munificent, opulent, splendid
ANTONYMS: skimpy, stingy, niggardly, spartan

20. ubiquitous
(yü bik' wə təs)

(*adj.*) present or existing everywhere

The _____ eye of the TV camera threatens to rob citizens of any sense of privacy.

SYNONYMS: pervasive, universal
ANTONYMS: restricted, limited, rare, scarce

Choosing the Right Word

Select the **boldface** word that better completes each sentence. You might refer to the selection on pages 60–61 to see how most of these words are used in context.

1. Cleopatra took her own life rather than suffer the (**figment, ignominy**) of being led through the streets of Rome in chains.

2. Her imagination is like a (**fecund, depraved**) field in which new ideas spring up like so many ripe ears of corn.

3. Scandal and corruption may so (**enervate, delineate**) an administration that it can no longer function effectively.

4. Two synonyms are rarely exactly the same because (**fiats, nuances**) of tone or applicability make each of the words unique.

5. Few writers have J. D. Salinger's remarkable ability to (**delineate, garner**) the emotions and aspirations of the average teenager.

A relief of Cleopatra, the last ruler of ancient Egypt (51 BC–30 BC).

6. It is only in superior mental powers, not in physical strength or (**ignominy, acuity**) of the senses, that human beings surpass other living things.

7. Your language is indeed clever and amusing, but your argument is nothing but a piece of outright (**sophistry, idiosyncrasy**).

8. Someone with a pronounced (**penchant, figment**) for saying the wrong thing might justly be described as a victim of "foot-in-mouth" disease.

9. The (**sumptuous, ubiquitous**) banquet was a pleasant change of pace from the spartan fare to which I had become accustomed.

10. He means well, but we cannot tolerate his highly (**idiosyncratic, fecund**) behavior in an organization that depends on discipline and teamwork.

11. Like a true fanatic, he considers anyone who disagrees with him on any issue to be either feebleminded or (**depraved, mundane**).

12. A true sign of intellectual maturity is the ability to distinguish the (**figments, penchants**) of wishful thinking from reality.

13. In a democracy, the government must rule by persuasion and consent—not by mere (**fiat, sophistry**).

14. How I'd love to knock the wind out of the sails of that lout's (**fecund, overweening**) conceit!

15. The conversation between the computer programmers was so (**esoteric, ubiquitous**) that I wasn't sure they were speaking English.

16. In that rarefied atmosphere, I was afraid to ask about anything quite so (**sumptuous, mundane**) as the location of the rest room.

17. I appreciate all those kind expressions of gratitude for my services, but I had hoped also to (**garner, nuance**) some cash.

18. The alert defense put up by our team completely neutralized our opponents' (**reputedly, sumptuously**) unstoppable passing attack.

19. We will never abandon a cause that has been (**garnered, hallowed**) by the achievements and sacrifices of so many noble people.

20. Probably no complaint of young people is more (**ubiquitous, depraved**) than "My parents don't understand me!"

21. In Shakespeare's *Othello* and *King Lear*, the (**overweening, sumptuous**) pride of the title characters contributes to their tragic downfalls.

22. Eight White Sox players in the 1919 World Series were banned from baseball for throwing games and forced to live with the (**fiat, ignominy**) of their actions.

23. The orator who is most able to recognize and rebut his or her opponent's persuasive (**figments, sophistry**) consistently will win the debate.

24. Weary of her (**mundane, ubiquitous**) day-to-day life, the woman embarked on a summer-long bicycle adventure across the continental United States.

25. Given my (**penchant, nuance**) for spicy food, I should enjoy the cayenne pepper.

 **Synonyms**

*Choose the word from this unit that is the same or most nearly the same in meaning as the **boldface** word or expression in the phrase. Write that word on the line. Use a dictionary if necessary.*

1. known for his **propensity** for exaggeration _____

2. as a result of a general **edict** _____

3. a **supposed** heir to a huge fortune _____

4. an **eccentricity** of speech _____

5. **depicted** the view from the balcony _____

6. sought **occult** knowledge in ancient books _____

7. the latest **creation** of his imagination _____

8. their **omnipresent** sense of dread _____

9. known for the **keenness** of her wit _____

10. the **dishonor** of plagiarism _____

Antonyms

*Choose the word from this unit that is most nearly opposite in meaning to the **boldface** word or expression in the phrase. Write that word on the line. Use a dictionary if necessary.*

1. a man of **modest** aspirations _____

2. the **other worldly** side of life _____

3. made a **meager** meal _____

4. the **glory** of her situation _____

5. believed the story was **reality** _____

Completing the Sentence

From the words in this unit, choose the one that best completes each of the following sentences. Write the word in the space provided.

1. The marathon not only brought in huge sums of money for Africa's starving masses, but also ___garnered___ much sympathy for their plight.

2. Beneath the man's cultivated manner and impeccable grooming there lurked the ___depraved___ mind of a brutal sadist.

3. The man is ___reputed___ to have mob connections, but so far no one has actually substantiated the allegation.

4. May I interrupt this abstruse discussion and turn your attention to more ___mundane___ matters—like what's for dinner?

5. Most people I know are so busy dealing with the ordinary problems of life that they have no time for ___esoteric___ philosophical speculation.

6. During the eleven years of his "personal rule," King Charles I bypassed Parliament and ruled England by royal ___fiat___.

7. Analysis will show that his "brilliant exposition" of how we can handle the pollution problem without cost to anyone is sheer ___sophistry___.

8. I was so ___enervated___ by the oppressive heat and humidity of that awful afternoon that I could barely move.

9. The phonograph is but one of the wonderful new devices that sprang from the ___fecund___ mind of Thomas Edison, our most prolific inventor.

10. "Your suspicion that I am constantly making fun of you behind your back is a mere ___figment___ of your overheated brain," I replied.

11. The ground in which those soldiers are buried was ___hallowed___ by the blood they shed on it.

12. He was a changed young man after he suffered the ___ignominy___ of expulsion from West Point for conduct unbecoming a gentleman.

13. His constant use of the word *fabulous*, even for quite ordinary subjects, is a(n) ___idiosyncrasy___ that I could do without.

14. There is quite a difference between the austere furnishings of my little apartment and the ___sumptuous___ accommodations of a luxury hotel.

15. His ___overweening___ sense of superiority dominates his personality in much the same way as his beetling brow dominates his face.

16. You may have many good traits, but I do not admire your ___penchant___ for borrowing things and failing to return them.

17. The passing years lessened her physical vigor but in no way diminished the ___acuity___ of her judgment.

18. Music can often express a(n) ___nuance___ of mood or feeling that would be difficult to put into words.

19. The artist's sketch not only ___delineates___ the model's appearance accurately, but also captured something of her personality.

20. American-style fast-food shops have gained such popularity all over the world that they are now truly ___ubiquitous___.

Writing: Words in Action

1. Look back at "What Is Pop Art?" (pages 60–61). Think about the kinds of art and music that are popular today. How have styles of art and music changed over the years? How do they reflect the social values and issues of a specific time period? Write a brief essay in which you analyze one or two current trends in art or music, explaining what they reveal about contemporary society. Use at least two details from the passage and three unit words in your analysis.

2. For centuries, people have tried to answer this question: "Is some art actually better than other art, or is the quality of a work of art really just a matter of personal taste?" What is your opinion? If there is good and bad art, then what makes good art good, and what makes bad art bad? Write at least three paragraphs explaining your viewpoint. Support your ideas with specific details from your reading (pages 60–61), your prior knowledge, and your personal experience and observations.

Vocabulary in Context

Literary Text

The following excerpts are from Charles Dickens's novel David Copperfield. *Some of the words you have studied in this unit appear in **boldface** type. Complete each statement below the excerpt by circling the letter of the correct answer.*

1. By and by, when we had dined in a **sumptuous** manner off boiled dabs, melted butter, and potatoes, with a chop for me, a hairy man with a very good-natured face came home.

   Something that is **sumptuous** is
   a. casual
   b. magnificent
   c. protracted
   d. companionable

2. "The victim, from my cradle, of pecuniary liabilities to which I have been unable to respond, I have ever been the sport and toy of debasing circumstances. **Ignominy,** Want, Despair, and Madness, have, collectively or separately, been the attendants of my career."

   Ignominy is
   a. disgrace
   b. poverty
   c. larceny
   d. imprisonment

3. "Miss Dartle," I returned, "you deepen the injury... you do him a great wrong."

   "I do him no wrong," she returned. "They are a **depraved**, worthless set."

   Someone who is **depraved** is definitely NOT
   a. reasonable
   b. dynamic
   c. cheerful
   d. moral

A scene from the 1935 film version of *David Copperfield*, starring W.C. Fields as Mr. Micawber and Freddie Bartholomew as David Copperfield.

4. Before this boy, who was **reputed** to be a great scholar, and was very good-looking, and at least half-a-dozen years my senior, I was carried as before a magistrate.

   A person who is **reputed** to be a scholar is
   a. generally believed to be one
   b. expected to become one
   c. humble about his abilities
   d. devoted to his studies

5. What other changes have come upon me, besides the changes in my growth and looks, and in the knowledge I have **garnered** all this while?

   When something is **garnered**, it is
   a. verified
   b. gathered
   c. utilized
   d. dispersed

Interactive Quiz

Snap the code, or go to
vocabularyworkshop.com

Read the following selection, taking note of the **boldface** words and their contexts. These words are among those you will be studying in Unit 6. As you complete the exercises in this unit, it may help to refer to the way the words are used below.

Your Papers, Please
<Debate>

Today's debate question is: Should every citizen of the United States be required to have a national identity card?

Tessa: The United States should implement a national identity card system without delay. Failure to do so would make the government **derelict** in its duty to protect citizens, as well as constitute a **travesty** of common sense. The most compelling argument favoring national ID cards is the crucial, ongoing effort to forestall any terrorist attacks against the United States. Advocates of national ID cards have noted with **perspicacity** that our existing system of **surveillance** has been proved inadequate and has failed in the past to detect the **complicity** of the terrorists in plots against the Unites States.

Tyrone: All that glitters is not gold, Tessa, and establishment of a national ID card would be an **abject** surrender of civil liberties and our citizens' right to privacy. At the risk of sounding **testy**, I firmly dispute the implicit assumption that an ID card system would have foiled previous terrorist attacks. That conjecture is an illusion in this high-tech world, where forgery, hacking, and identity theft might well have equipped terrorists with fake cards.

Tessa: I believe a national ID card would have several **indubitable** benefits, Tyrone. First, it would offer consistency, in contrast to the varying requirements of the states for the issue of driver's licenses. Second, an ID card system could be administered with **equity**. Despite the **diatribes** of privacy advocates against such a system,

an effective ID card setup could operate with only five basic elements: name, address, Social Security number, photograph, and a finger or retinal print matching a chip on the card. Even a civil liberties **neophyte** would hesitate before raising an **indictment** of such requirements.

Tyrone: Tessa, people's right to privacy is the most important **motif** in my critique of a national ID card system, as there are numerous unresolved questions about the elements, requirements, and circumstances of an ID card program. All these questions would affect privacy: Would the program be voluntary or mandatory, for example? Who could lawfully demand presentation of the card, and on what occasions? Should the card be local, federal, or international? How much information could the government collect?

To ignore the risk of a slippery slope here would be **inane**. In the information age, everyone knows the extent to which giant institutions tend to assemble more and more data on citizens, sometimes for illegitimate purposes.

Tessa: I have several more arguments, Tyrone—the first of which is with a national ID card system concerns about racial and ethnic profiling would no longer be **moot**, because such concerns would be nullified by the uniformities of the card system. **Intermittent** harassment of minority groups would thus in all likelihood decline. Finally, many other countries, especially in Europe, use national ID cards successfully, so why not here?

Tyrone: A national ID card system would grant a single institution, the federal government, **plenary** powers to accrue information on all American citizens, so the potential for abuse is discernible. Contrary to your assertion, Tessa, racial profiling might actually increase. In other parts of the world with this system, the police are often entitled to demand

presentation of the card on the threat of arrest. The misuse of ID cards under totalitarian governments such as in South Africa, the former Soviet Union, and China has long been known. Let's consider carefully before we go down that path.

Snap the code, or go to **vocabularyworkshop.com**

Left: A foreign national ID card; Right: fraudulent government documents seized by U.S. Customs in New York

Definitions

Note the spelling, pronunciation, part(s) of speech, and definition(s) of each of the following words. Then write the word in the blank spaces in the illustrative sentence(s) following. Finally, study the lists of synonyms and antonyms.

1. abject
(ab′ jekt)

(*adj.*) degraded; base, contemptible; cringing, servile; complete and unrelieved

In the American dream, those who work hard can escape lives of _____ poverty.

SYNONYMS: wretched, miserable, ignoble, sheer, utter
ANTONYMS: noble, exalted

2. agnostic
(ag näs′ tik)

(*n.*) one who believes that nothing can be known about God; a skeptic; (*adj.*) without faith, skeptical

Although he was a confirmed _____, he supported the rights of others to practice their religion.

Her _____ tendencies made it difficult for her to subscribe to any set of religious beliefs.

SYNONYM: (*n.*) doubter
ANTONYM: (*n.*) believer

3. complicity
(kəm plis′ ə tē)

(*n.*) involvement in wrongdoing; the state of being an accomplice

If you know a crime is going to be committed but do nothing to prevent it, you may be accused of _____.

SYNONYMS: connivance, collusion
ANTONYMS: noninvolvement, innocence

4. derelict
(der′ ə likt)

(*n.*) someone or something that is abandoned or neglected; (*adj.*) left abandoned; neglectful of duty

The family complained about the unsightly collection of _____ cars in its neighbor's driveway.

SYNONYMS: (*n.*) vagrant; (*adj.*) delinquent
ANTONYMS: (*adj.*) punctilious, conscientious, scrupulous

5. diatribe
(dī′ ə trīb)

(*n.*) a bitter and prolonged verbal attack

The senator's speech was more of a _____ than a reasoned address.

SYNONYMS: harangue, tirade
ANTONYMS: panegyric, encomium, eulogy

6. effigy
(ef′ ə jē)

(*n.*) a crude image of a despised person

The night before the battle, the troops burned the despised enemy leader in _____.

SYNONYMS: figure, figurine

7. equity
(ek' wət ē)

(*n.*) the state or quality of being just, fair, or impartial; fair and equal treatment; something that is fair; the money value of a property above and beyond any mortgage or other claim

Prompted by considerations of _____, the father decided to divide his estate equally among his children.

SYNONYMS: justice, fairness, impartiality
ANTONYMS: unfairness, bias, prejudice

8. inane
(in ān')

(*adj.*) silly, empty of meaning or value

The politician made an _____ reply to the interviewer's probing question.

SYNONYMS: idiotic, moronic, fatuous
ANTONYMS: sensible, meaningful, profound

9. indictment
(in dīt' mənt)

(*n.*) the act of accusing; a formal accusation

The grand jury delivered the _____.

SYNONYMS: charge, accusation

10. indubitable
(in dü' bə tə bəl)

(*adj.*) certain, not to be doubted or denied

You cannot argue with _____ truths.

SYNONYMS: unquestionable, indisputable
ANTONYMS: questionable, debatable, dubious

11. intermittent
(in tər mit' ənt)

(*adj.*) stopping and beginning again, sporadic

She had _____ back pains for a week.

SYNONYMS: fitful, spasmodic, random
ANTONYM: uninterrupted

12. moot
(müt)

(*adj.*) open to discussion and debate, unresolved; (*v.*) to bring up for discussion; (*n.*) a hypothetical law case argued by students

The class agreed that the question of whether Jefferson should have retaliated sooner against the Barbary pirates was a _____ point.

The committee members decided to _____ the issue to the full Congress at the earliest opportunity.

The law student prepared for the _____.

SYNONYMS: (*adj.*) debatable, questionable; (*v.*) broach
ANTONYMS: (*adj.*) undebatable, indisputable, self-evident

13. motif
(mō tēf')

(*n.*) a principal idea, feature, theme, or element; a repeated or dominant figure in a design

The collector admired the unusual Asian _____ woven into the tapestry.

14. neophyte
(nē' ə fīt)

(*n.*) a new convert, beginner, novice

In comparison to an experienced wilderness hiker, he is a mere _____ in the woods.

SYNONYMS: tenderfoot, tyro
ANTONYMS: veteran, past master, expert, pro

15. perspicacity
(pər spə kas' ət ē)

(*n.*) keenness in observing and understanding

The bird watcher scans the surrounding trees and fields with the same _____ as a hawk looking for prey.

SYNONYMS: acumen, discernment
ANTONYMS: dullness, obtuseness

16. plenary
(plēn' ə rē)

(*adj.*) complete in all aspects or essentials; absolute; attended by all qualified members

Because of its importance, the case was presented at a _____ session of the Superior Court.

SYNONYM: unrestricted
ANTONYMS: limited, restricted, incomplete

17. surveillance
(sər vā' ləns)

(*n.*) a watch kept over a person; careful, close, and disciplined observation

The police kept the suspect under strict _____ after she was released.

SYNONYMS: observation, monitoring

18. sylvan
(sil' vən)

(*adj.*) pertaining to or characteristic of forests; living or located in a forest; wooded, woody

Once upon a time, Hansel and Gretel walked down a _____ path, leaving only bread crumbs.

SYNONYM: arcadian

19. testy
(tes' tē)

(*adj.*) easily irritated; characterized by impatience and exasperation

The lawyer's _____ remarks during cross-examination probably affected her credibility with the jury.

SYNONYMS: irritable, peevish, waspish, petulant
ANTONYMS: imperturbable, unexcitable

20. travesty
(trav' ə stē)

(*n.*) a grotesque or grossly inferior imitation; a disguise, especially the clothing of the opposite sex; (*v.*) to ridicule by imitating in a broad or burlesque fashion

Instead of modernizing Shakespeare's *Twelfth Night*, they made a _____ of it.

The new song _____ the original version.

SYNONYMS: (*n.*) burlesque, caricature, farce

Choosing the Right Word

Select the **boldface** word that better completes each sentence. You might refer to the selection on pages 70–71 to see how most of these words are used in context.

1. Human and animal forms carved in stucco and stone are a common (**motif, neophyte**) in ancient Aztec art.

2. Though the book was written by an avowed (**agnostic, derelict**), it enjoyed a certain popularity with religious types.

3. As he sat before the fire reading his newspaper, Grandfather seemed the very epitome of (**plenary, sylvan**) contentment.

4. Because she is a fair-minded woman, I'm sure she will present both sides of the controversy with admirable (**equity, effigy**).

5. Though I can sometimes be as (**testy, derelict**) as an irate wasp, I normally do not lose my temper very easily.

The Aztec calendar marked a sacred year of 260 days.

6. Today's forecast calls for variable cloudiness with (**abject, intermittent**) periods of rain.

7. My studies have convinced me that the one dominant (**motif, diatribe**) in American history has been the expansion of democracy.

8. Bag ladies and other homeless (**neophytes, derelicts**) roam our streets in increasing numbers.

9. The awkward pause in the conversation became even more painful when he interjected his (**plenary, inane**) attempts at humor.

10. All of a sudden, a strange young man rushed onto the speaker's platform and launched into a (**travesty, diatribe**) against "big government."

11. After over 30 years in Congress, he retains the idealism of the (**agnostic, neophyte**) but has gained the practical wisdom of the veteran.

12. His disgraceful behavior since he left college is in itself a(n) (**indictment, surveillance**) of the lax, overindulgent upbringing he received.

13. What qualities will he have to fall back on when his (**indubitable, testy**) charm and good looks begin to wear thin?

14. His extraordinary ability to (**moot, travesty**) the works of popular writers is largely due to his keen eye for the ridiculous.

15. The picture shows the three Graces dancing in a forest clearing, while nymphs, satyrs, and other (**sylvan, indubitable**) creatures cavort among the trees.

16. According to that village's custom, one can get rid of an enemy by making a tiny (**effigy, motif**) of him and sticking it full of pins.

17. Observers on the ground keep close (**surveillance, equity**) on air traffic at a busy airport by means of various electronic devices, such as radar.

18. Only an (**intermittent, abject**) coward would stand idly by while a defenseless old woman was mugged in the street.

19. The historian had long been noted for the soundness of his scholarship and the (**complicity, perspicacity**) of his judgment.

20. "I vetoed that idea when it was first (**mooted, indicted**) years ago," the governor said, "and I have never regretted my decision."

21. How can I be accused of (**indictment, complicity**) in that plot when I did not even know the conspirators?

22. To some readers, the dark and (**intermittent, sylvan**) setting of Hawthorne's short story "Young Goodman Brown" symbolizes the unknown.

23. We laughed at Grandmother's confession that she can be (**testy, moot**) before she has her morning cup of coffee.

24. Several theology professors have given provocative reviews of the new book by Mr. Stuart, who readily admits he is an (**effigy, agnostic**).

25. The sleeping security guard was (**derelict, plenary**) in his duties.

Synonyms

*Choose the word from this unit that is the same or most nearly the same in meaning as the **boldface** word or expression in the phrase. Write that word on the line. Use a dictionary if necessary.*

1. a crude **likeness** _____

2. put under **scrutiny** _____

3. their level of **involvement** _____

4. the **forested** slopes of the Rockies _____

5. admired for his uncommon **acuity** _____

6. was given **unlimited** power to govern _____

7. indoctrinated the **rookie** _____

8. a questioning **nonbeliever** _____

9. **remiss** in discharging her responsibilities _____

10. the **vapid** chatter of thoughtless critics _____

Antonyms

*Choose the word from this unit that is most nearly opposite in meaning to the **boldface** word or expression in the phrase. Write that word on the line. Use a dictionary if necessary.*

1. **nonparticipation** as partners _____

2. being very **clever** _____

3. painted the **treeless** landscape _____

4. pleased the **devout** _____

5. noticed the **flattering copy** _____

Completing the Sentence

From the words in this unit, choose the one that best completes each of the following sentences. Write the word in the space provided.

1. During the emergency, the mayor assumed ___plenary___ authority and did whatever was needed to provide essential services.

2. Those who saw the young woman being assaulted and did nothing to help her were guilty of ___complicity___ in the crime.

3. The ___perspicacity___ of her analysis not only clarified the nature of the problem but also suggested its most promising solution.

4. Though some writers have emphasized Jefferson's human weaknesses, his greatness is also a(n) ___indubitable___ part of the historical record.

5. I would be ___derelict___ in my duty to you if I did not warn you against the pernicious effects of smoking cigarettes.

6. For years, we carried on a(n) ___intermittent___ correspondence, sometimes allowing months to pass before a letter was answered.

7. How could a mere ___neophyte___ in the teaching profession question the judgment of so experienced an educator?

8. The fact that so many released prisoners return to a life of crime is in itself a terrifying ___indictment___ of our penal system.

9. Throughout the period that the spy thought he had gone undetected, he was actually under close ___surveillance___ by the CIA.

10. Since the accused was never really given a chance to defend himself, his so-called trial was nothing but a(n) ___travesty___ of justice.

11. "Simple ___equity___ demands that we distribute the tax burden as fairly as possible among the populace," the senator remarked.

12. Since he neither affirms nor denies the existence of God, I'd classify him as a(n) ___agnostic___ rather than an atheist.

13. Every time we did something to anger him, he delivered an intemperate ___diatribe___ lambasting our "hopeless irresponsibility."

14. It was such a(n) ___inane___ remark that I couldn't keep myself from laughing derisively when I heard it.

15. I'd say that the phrase "having a short fuse" aptly describes my boss's decidedly ___testy___ disposition.

16. In her garland of leaves and acorns, the child looked very much like some ___sylvan___ spirit from an Arthurian myth.

17. The overthrown dictator was hanged in ___effigy___ before a vast throng in the town square.

18. At the slightest sound of thunder, my dog Rover dives under the bed in a state of ___abject___ terror.

19. In Wagner's operas, brief musical ___motifs___ associated with the characters or their actions recur again and again.

20. How can you call that a(n) ___moot___ question when it is quite clearly a simple matter of right and wrong?

Writing: Words in Action

1. Look back at "Your Papers, Please" (pages 70–71). Think about the arguments offered by each side in the debate. Do you believe every U.S. citizen should be required to have a national identity card? Write a persuasive essay that identifies and supports your position on this issue. Use at least two details from the passage and three unit words to support your argument.

2. Legal and ethical concerns about a person's right to privacy that are part of the debate about a national ID also extend into issues in the workplace. For example, do employers have the right to monitor their employees' workplace use of the Internet (such as email and social media)? Write an essay of at least three paragraphs in which you discuss the advantages and disadvantages of such monitoring. Draw on specific examples from your own observations, studies, reading (refer to pages 70–71), or personal experiences, and use three or more words from this unit.

Vocabulary in Context

Literary Text

The following excerpts are from Joseph Conrad's novels Victory *and* Nostromo. *Some of the words you have studied in this unit appear in **boldface** type. Complete each statement below the excerpt by circling the letter of the correct answer.*

1. He felt intensely aware of her personality, as if this were the first moment of leisure he had found to look at her since they had come together. The peculiar timbre of her voice, with its modulations of audacity and sadness, would have given interest to the most **inane** chatter. But she was no chatterer. (*Victory*)

   Something that is **inane** is definitely NOT

   a. enjoyable   c. surprising
   b. meaningful   d. boring

2. He leaned his back against one of the lofty uprights which still held up the company's signboard above the mound of **derelict** coal. Nobody could have guessed how much his blood was up. (*Victory*)

   Something that is **derelict** is

   a. filthy   c. useless
   b. primeval   d. abandoned

3. But Don Jose, disregarding the general **indictment** as though he had not heard a word of it, took up the defense of Barrios. The man was competent enough for his special task in the plan of campaign. (*Nostromo*)

   An **indictment** is a(n)

   a. perspective   c. slander
   b. strategy   d. accusation

4. Not to have bound and gagged him seemed to Decoud now the height of improvident folly. As long as the miserable creature had the power to raise a yell he was a constant danger. His **abject** terror was mute now, but there was no saying from what cause it might suddenly find vent in shrieks. (*Nostromo*)

   Terror that is **abject** is

   a. unjustified   c. unrelieved
   b. sporadic   d. conspicuous

5. The necessity of winding round his little finger, almost daily, the pompous and **testy** self-importance of the old seaman had grown irksome with use to Nostromo. (*Nostromo*)

   Someone who is **testy** is

   a. sly   c. greedy
   b. exasperating   d. dull

Considered a great English novelist and short story writer, the Polish-born Joseph Conrad began learning English at age twenty.

Interactive Quiz

Snap the code, or go to
vocabularyworkshop.com

Vocabulary for Comprehension

*Read the following selection in which some of the words you have studied in Units 4–6 appear in **boldface** type. Then answer the questions on page 81.*

As this passage shows, zoos have served a wide range of purposes during their long history.

(Line)

Zoos, or at least collections of **incarcerated** animals, have existed for millennia. The purpose of capturing and caging animals,
(5) however, has changed over time. In ancient Egypt, certain animals were deified or else considered very closely connected to gods. These animals were held in cages in temple
(10) complexes and treated as objects of worship. In a sense, these ancient zoos were **hallowed** grounds, but it is difficult not to see them as existing more for the benefit of humans than
(15) for animals. In the classical world, private menageries, or collections of exotic animals, were **ubiquitous** among **overweening** rulers who wished to advertise their power and
(20) wealth.

The modern conception of a zoo emerged in Victorian England. In fact, the word *zoo* derives from the London zoological garden, which
(25) was established in the late nineteenth century. The purpose of this zoo, according to its founder Sir Stamford Raffles, was scientific study, not the "vulgar admiration" of
(30) animals. Despite Raffles's **fiat**, however, zoos on both sides of the Atlantic soon focused on entertaining the large crowds that paid money to view the animals.
(35) While exposure to both rare and commonplace creatures benefited many zoo patrons, the animals often suffered. The creatures, which had been either taken captive in the wild
(40) or bred in captivity, were usually housed singly in tiny metal cages or other bare enclosures, where they paced nervously or lay **recumbent** in a bored stupor.
(45) Finally, with the rise of ecological consciousness in the 1970s, the bars began to come down in zoos all over the world. Increasingly, captive animals were placed in roomier,
(50) more natural environments not only for their own well-being but also as a way of educating the public about the need to preserve wild habitats.

1. The meaning of **incarcerated** (line 2) is
   a. imaginary
   b. confined
   c. immense
   d. exotic
   e. dangerous

2. The primary purpose of the passage is
   a. to present some aspects of the historical development of zoos
   b. to offer insights into the religion of ancient Egypt
   c. to compare modern zoos with ancient ones
   d. to argue that zoos unjustifiably deprive wild animals of their freedom
   e. to expose the shocking conditions in modern zoos

3. **Hallowed** (line 12) most nearly means
   a. forbidden
   b. breeding
   c. fertile
   d. sacred
   e. neutral

4. **Ubiquitous** (line 17) is best defined as
   a. prohibited
   b. pervasive
   c. coveted
   d. traditional
   e. unusual

5. The meaning of **overweening** (line 18) is
   a. weak
   b. benevolent
   c. feuding
   d. arrogant
   e. brutal

6. According to the author, in the classical world private menageries of exotic animals served to
   a. entertain large crowds of visitors
   b. strengthen traditional religious attitudes
   c. advertise the power and wealth of rulers
   d. celebrate foreign conquests
   e. insure the progress of science

7. The author states that the modern conception of a zoo emerged
   a. in China around 1900
   b. during the late Middle Ages in France
   c. in Victorian England
   d. in the United States during the late nineteenth century
   e. during the Italian Renaissance

8. From paragraph 2 (lines 21–44), one can reasonably infer that the author
   a. rejects the techniques of captive breeding
   b. thinks that zoos are vital for scientific progress
   c. thinks that zoos should be abolished
   d. believes that zoo admission should be free
   e. sympathizes with the animals' suffering

9. **Fiat** (line 30) most nearly means
   a. decree
   b. opinion
   c. title
   d. request
   e. wealth

10. The organization of the passage as a whole is best defined as
    a. comparison and contrast
    b. chronological order
    c. cause and effect
    d. spatial order
    e. order of importance

11. **Recumbent** (line 43) most nearly means
    a. contented
    b. ignored
    c. injured
    d. prostrate
    e. relaxed

12. The tone of the final paragraph (lines 45–53) is best described as
    a. humorous
    b. philosophical
    c. positive
    d. satirical
    e. skeptical

Two-Word Completions

Select the pair of words that best complete the meaning of each of the following passages.

1. I'm extremely circumspect about what I say or do in the office because my boss is so _____ that it is easy to _____ or exasperate him.

   a. mordant . . . disarray
   b. abject . . . moot

   c. testy . . . nettle
   d. jocular . . . enervate

2. Edward R. Murrow will hold a place in history as a journalist who saw in 1950s television the potential to educate, and not simply to entertain. He felt it was the _____ responsibility of all journalists to act as a(n) _____ against both zealotry and indifference.

   a. consummate . . . fiat
   b. plenary . . . grouse

   c. overweening . . . indictment
   d. incumbent . . . bastion

3. Vincent van Gogh was indeed a(n) _____ technician, able to _____ every nuance of nature's variegated panorama with a mere stroke of the brush.

   a. ubiquitous . . . hallow
   b. indubitable . . . enervate

   c. consummate . . . delineate
   d. sylvan . . . travesty

4. Despite the harried officer's _____ attempts to steady his troops after the left flank had been turned, they fled from the field in such _____ that their departure was more of a rout than a retreat.

   a. consummate . . . ignominy
   b. ludicrous . . . equity

   c. intermittent . . . concord
   d. frenetic . . . disarray

5. After the battle, the officer who had failed to carry out his orders was arrested by the military police, charged with _____ of duty, and _____ in the stockade, pending a court-martial.

   a. atrophy . . . garnered
   b. dereliction . . . incarcerated

   c. travesty . . . mooted
   d. ignominy . . . hallowed

6. Although the man is certainly thought to have been involved in the crime, no _____ has yet been brought against him because the authorities have not been able to assemble enough evidence to establish his _____ beyond a reasonable doubt.

   a. indictment . . . complicity
   b. surveillance . . . equity

   c. exigency . . . acuity
   d. figment . . . perspicacity

7. The wealthy widow had a(n) _____ for fine clothes and _____ meals.

   a. stratagem . . . pecuniary
   b. flotsam . . . fecund

   c. acuity . . . recumbent
   d. penchant . . . sumptuous

Adages

In the essay "What Is Pop Art?" (see pages 60–61), the author uses the old saying "Beauty is in the eye of the beholder."

"Beauty is in the eye of the beholder" is an example of an adage. An **adage** is a traditional saying that many people accept as true. Adages offer a condensed, general observation about human nature and experience. They may be humorous or profound and frequently use memorable figures of speech. The adage "Beauty is in the eye of the beholder" emphasizes that each individual's perception of beauty is unique. It suggests that a person's judgment that something or someone is beautiful is subjective. What one person finds beautiful, another might not.

Choosing the Right Adage

Read each sentence. Use context clues to figure out the meaning of each adage in **boldface** *print. Then write the letter of the definition for the adage in the sentence.*

1. When Kim missed the bus a second time, she muttered, "**When it rains, it pours**." _____

2. "**Mind your p's and q's**," called Mr. Rose to his three young children as they began pulling boxes from the grocery store shelves. _____

3. I told my best friend, "**Don't put the cart before the horse**; get a job before you buy a new car." _____

4. If Erin will **let bygones be bygones**, she can save her friendship with Alex. _____

5. The housepainter was tempted to rush, but he knew that **a stitch in time saves nine**. _____

6. After the election, the losing candidate's daughter whispered to her father, "**Keep your chin up**." _____

7. When my grandfather said he wanted to start blogging, my grandmother laughed and reminded him that **you can't teach an old dog new tricks**. _____

8. After ignoring residents' concerns about traffic, the mayor finally pledged to **grab the bull by the horns**. _____

9. It would be risky to appoint a new general since the war is not over; **do not change horses midstream**. _____

10. Uncle John said he knew Jennifer would receive the scholarship because **cream always rises to the top**. _____

a. Forget about past disagreements.

b. Doing things right initially will save time later.

c. Tackle the problem directly and confidently.

d. Remain cheerful during difficult times.

e. Something very good will eventually attract attention.

f. Misfortunes rarely come alone.

g. Do things in the proper order.

h. As people age, it becomes harder to learn new skills.

i. Behave properly.

j. It's unwise to change leaders during a crisis.

Writing with Adages

Find the meaning of each adage. (Use an online or print dictionary if necessary.) Then write a sentence for each adage.

1. Virtue is its own reward.

_____

2. Charity begins at home.

_____

3. Waste not, want not.

_____

4. Drastic times call for drastic measures.

_____

5. The proof of the pudding is in the eating.

_____

_____

6. When the cat's away, the mice will play.

_____

_____

7. Don't cut off your nose to spite your face.

_____

_____

8. Every rose has its thorn.

_____

9. Money doesn't grow on trees.

_____

10. An empty purse frightens away friends.

_____

11. It's no use crying over spilt milk.

_____

12. Let the chips fall where they may.

_____

Denotation and Connotation

The **denotation** of a word—its definition—is objective. It can be found in the dictionary. Many words, however, have one or more subjective meanings. They are the emotional associations, or **connotations**, of a word. Connotations can be positive or negative.

By using words with different shades of meaning and connotations, writers and speakers can create and convey a precise mood or message. For instance, to emphasize the cleverness of two characters, a writer could describe them as *ingenious, astute,* or *resourceful*. To convey not only intelligence but also suggest a lack of candor, a writer might instead describe the characters as *cunning, sly,* or *wily*.

Consider these synonyms for the neutral word *intermittent:*

  sporadic   *variable*   *desultory*   *spasmodic*

Sporadic and *variable* have neutral or positive connotations, describing something occurring at irregular intervals. The negative connotations of *desultory* and *spasmodic* suggest that the lack of regularity is unfortunate, disappointing, or even violent.

> **Think:** An insomniac might look forward to taking sporadic or variable rests the next day, not desultory or spasmodic naps.

Look at these examples of words that are similar in denotation but have different connotations.

NEUTRAL	POSITIVE	NEGATIVE
utterance	tribute	diatribe
timid	retiring	pusillanimous
reasoning	sagacity	sophistry

Understanding the connotations of words with similar denotations is an important skill. It enables writers and speakers to get across their point more effectively and allows readers and listeners to understand meaning more precisely.

Shades of Meaning

Write a plus sign (+) in the box if the word has a positive connotation. Write a minus sign (−) if the word has a negative connotation. Put a zero (0) if the word is neutral.

1. disarray ☐   **2.** incumbent ☐   **3.** equity ☐   **4.** grouse ☐

5. sylvan ☐   **6.** atrophy ☐   **7.** overweening ☐   **8.** incarcerate ☐

9. jocular ☐   **10.** mordant ☐   **11.** pecuniary ☐   **12.** hallow ☐

13. enervate ☐   **14.** fecund ☐   **15.** perspicacity ☐   **16.** abject ☐

Expressing the Connotation

Read each sentence. Select the word in parentheses that expresses the connotation (positive, negative, or neutral) given at the beginning of the sentence.

positive 　**1.** In last Sunday's recital, the cellist's (**terminal, consummate**) performance of a Beethoven concerto surprised the audience.

neutral 　**2.** The hotel staff worked at a (**frenetic, bustling**) pace as the wedding guests began to arrive.

negative 　**3.** As they spilled into the streets, angry protestors displayed (**effigies, embodiments**) of the tyrannical dictator.

neutral 　**4.** The newspaper report hinted at the elderly woman's (**participation, complicity**) in the recent police investigation.

negative 　**5.** The girl is planning to (**imitate, travesty**) Shakespeare's sonnet by rewriting it as a limerick.

positive 　**6.** The chaperone was pleased by the cooperation and (**demeanor, concord**) her young students displayed on the field trip.

neutral 　**7.** One (**idiosyncrasy, flaw**) of William Faulkner's writing style is his use of long sentences with multiple independent and dependent clauses.

positive 　**8.** Sean's (**whimsical, inane**) comments about the film made me appreciate his unique wit.

Challenge: Using Connotation

Choose vocabulary words from Units 4–6 to replace the highlighted words in the sentences below. Then explain how the connotation of the replacement word changes the tone of the sentence.

fiat	agnostic	sumptuous
ignominy	penchant	testy

1. The busy librarian responded to the child's question in a **distracted**
_____ manner.
_____
_____

2. It has taken my brother years to live down the **embarrassment**
_____ of failing his driver's test the first three times he took it.
_____
_____

3. Guidebooks agree that the hotel's accommodations are among the most **expensive**
_____ in London.
_____
_____

Classical Roots

gno(s)—to know

The Greek root *gno(s)* appears in **agnostic** (page 72). The literal meaning is "one who does not know." In modern usage the word refers to an individual who believes that nothing can be known about God, or a skeptic.

cognate	cognizant	gnostic	prognosis
cognition	diagnose	ignore	recognize

From the list of words above, choose the one that corresponds to each of the brief definitions below. Write the word in the blank space in the illustrative sentence below the definition. Use an online or print dictionary if necessary.

1. a prediction of the probable course of a disease; a probable forecast or estimate
   With modern treatment options, patients who contract this once-fatal disease now have an excellent _____ for full recovery.

2. to identify a disease or condition based on observation, examination, and analysis
   A podiatrist is trained to _____ and treat a range of problems of the foot.

3. of, relating to, or possessing intellectual or spiritual knowledge
   Many religions observe a _____ doctrine, where emphasis is placed on the pursuit of spiritual and intellectual knowledge.

4. to disregard deliberately; to pay no attention to; to refuse to consider
   If we just _____ Rover, he will eventually stop begging for food at the table.

5. related by family or origin; related in nature, character, quality, or function; a person or thing related to another
   The Sanskrit word for king—*rajah*—is a _____ of the Latin *rex*.

6. the broad mental process by which knowledge is acquired, including aspects of awareness, perception, reasoning, judgment, memory, and intuition; knowledge
   After a serious blow to the head, her _____ was impaired for several weeks.

7. to know, identify, or show awareness of something from past experience or knowledge; to accept as a fact; to acknowledge a thing's existence, validity, or authority; to approve of or appreciate
   The school board has come to _____ the positive impact of art and music classes.

8. fully informed; conscious; aware
   As a result of a 1966 court decision, all arrested suspects must be made _____ of their Miranda rights.

*Read the following selection, taking note of the **boldface** words and their contexts. These words are among those you will be studying in Unit 7. As you complete the exercises in this unit, it may help to refer to the way the words are used below.*

John Lennon's Legacy

<Biographical Sketch>

John Lennon in 1961

John Lennon was born in Liverpool, England, on October 9, 1940, at the height of World War II. Forty years later, on December 8, 1980, he was shot dead by a mentally unstable fan outside his Manhattan apartment. During his short life, as a musician, artist, poet, and political activist, Lennon transcended his time. "If someone thinks that love and peace is a cliché that must have been left behind in the '60s, that's his problem," he said. "Love and peace are eternal."

Lennon's father left his wife and young son before World War II ended. Poor but never **indigent**, Lennon's mother, Julia, entrusted the boy to her sister, Mimi, one of a **coterie** of "five strong, intelligent sisters," as Lennon later recalled. During his childhood, Lennon spent an **inordinate** amount of time with **convivial** female relatives. In later years, he said that this was his "first feminist education" and that living apart from his parents enabled him "to see that parents are not gods" but were human and had flaws just like everyone else.

Despite their living apart, Julia Lennon maintained a close relationship with her son. She encouraged his interest in music, rather than demand that he **jettison** his musical aspirations (as his Aunt Mimi hoped he would do), even giving him his first guitar when he was fifteen. The gift was **felicitous**, as Lennon dove into music with **pertinacious** ambition. His belief that it would bring him lasting fame was as strong as Aunt Mimi's conviction that his hopes were **illusory**.

Lennon soon realized his dream of fame, thanks to the success of the Beatles, the band he formed with his songwriting **counterpart**, Paul McCartney. The band rocketed to fame in the early 1960s, propelled by energetic pop songs like "Love Me Do," simple variations on the time-honored theme of teenage love.

With age comes wisdom. As Lennon's artistic vision matured, he led the Beatles toward new horizons, and his lyrics increasingly contained intricate metaphors and political themes. Lennon's humor, free spirit, and politics soon permeated the band's image and music, a transformation marked by the album *Sgt. Pepper's Lonely Hearts Club Band*. The album cover ridicules military formality, presenting the bandmates in **garish** uniforms, **raiment** that was absurd even for its era. Lennon's maturing talents shine in songs like "A Day in the Life," which weaves themes of class and political

The Beatles in the BBC's *Top of the Pops* television show in June 1966

John Lennon and Yoko Ono, his wife, in a war protest, London, 1969.

power with images of mundane and tragic moments in life; the lyrics are a dreamlike tapestry **embellished** with metaphor. Critics soon acknowledged Lennon as a worthy moden poet.

Politics and poetry remained at the fore of Lennon's songwriting as he became a high-profile social activist. U.S. leaders, mired in the Vietnam War, objected to the **effrontery** of this popular British "peacenik," and had him monitored by the FBI, which diligently collected **picayune** details for his file. Lennon did little to **allay** their concerns. Many of his lyrics, such as those in "All You Need Is Love" and later, "Imagine," rallied those who **demurred** violence. As a group, the Beatles proved more **ephemeral** than their fame, and personal tensions broke up the band. Yet Lennon continued to speak passionately against violence and enmity with solo works like "Give Peace a Chance."

"We're not being unreasonable. Just saying 'give it a chance,'" said Lennon in 1980 when discussing his desire for a world without war. With "Imagine," he was asking for a world without hate, greed, or hunger. "It's the same message over and over. And it's positive," he said of his work. Lennon's devotion to such positive messages, his willingness to use his art and fame to promote love and peace among all people, is his most enduring legacy.

Snap the code, or go to
vocabularyworkshop.com

Definitions

Note the spelling, pronunciation, part(s) of speech, and definition(s) of each of the following words. Then write the word in the blank spaces in the illustrative sentence(s) following. Finally, study the lists of synonyms and antonyms.

1. allay
(ə lā′)

(*v.*) to calm or pacify, set to rest; to lessen or relieve

The politician made a speech in order to

_____ his constituents' fears.

SYNONYMS: reduce, alleviate, moderate
ANTONYMS: aggravate, exacerbate, intensify

2. bestial
(bes′ chəl)

(*adj.*) beastlike; beastly, brutal; subhuman in intelligence and sensibility

In beating their prisoner, the guards were guilty of a truly

_____ act.

SYNONYMS: animalistic, loathsome
ANTONYMS: human, clement, virtuous, upright

3. convivial
(kən viv′ ē əl)

(*adj.*) festive, sociable, having fun together, genial

Thanksgiving dinner at Grandmother's house is always a

_____ family gathering.

SYNONYMS: fun-loving, jovial, merry
ANTONYMS: dour, sullen, unsociable

4. coterie
(kō′ tə rē)

(*n.*) a circle of acquaintances; a close-knit, often exclusive, group of people with a common interest

Robert Browning and his _____ had ideas about poetry that seemed revolutionary in their day.

SYNONYMS: clique, set

5. counterpart
(kaủnt′ ər pärt)

(*n.*) a person or thing closely resembling or corresponding to another; a complement

I have to admit I was frightened of my

_____ on the other team because she held the high-jump record.

SYNONYM: match

6. demur
(di mər′)

(*v.*) to object or take exception to; (*n.*) an objection

The rank and file will _____ if they are not consulted regularly by the union leadership.

The speech in favor of the proposal was drowned out by a chorus of _____ from the senate floor.

SYNONYMS: (*v.*) protest, object to
ANTONYMS: (*v.*) assent to, consent to, accept, agree to

7. effrontery
(ə frən' tə rē)

(*n.*) shameless boldness, impudence

After having been suspended for disrespectful behavior, the student had the _____ to talk back to his teacher again.

SYNONYMS: chutzpah, nerve, impertinence, cheek
ANTONYMS: shyness, diffidence, timidity

8. embellish
(em bel' ish)

(*v.*) to decorate, adorn, touch up; to improve by adding details

The best storytellers _____ their tales in ways that help readers visualize the setting.

SYNONYM: garnish
ANTONYMS: strip, mar, disfigure

9. ephemeral
(i fem' ər əl)

(*adj.*) lasting only a short time, short-lived

Only the greatest of writers and artists achieve anything other than _____ popularity.

SYNONYMS: transient, evanescent, transitory
ANTONYMS: durable, long-lasting, permanent, perpetual

10. felicitous
(fə lis' ə təs)

(*adj.*) appropriate, apt, well chosen; marked by well-being or good fortune, happy

In view of the high prices for home heating oil, the mild winter was a _____ turn of events.

SYNONYMS: fortunate, well-put
ANTONYMS: inappropriate, inept, graceless, unhappy

11. furtive
(fər' tiv)

(*adj.*) done slyly or stealthily, sneaky, secret, shifty; stolen

The girl was caught taking a _____ glance at the test paper of the student sitting next to her.

SYNONYMS: covert, surreptitious
ANTONYMS: aboveboard, open

12. garish
(gar' ish)

(*adj.*) glaring; tastelessly showy or overdecorated in a vulgar or offensive way

The storefront was painted in _____ colors so that it would attract the attention of passersby.

SYNONYMS: gaudy, flashy, tawdry
ANTONYMS: subdued, muted, understated, quiet

13. illusory
(i lü' sə rē)

(*adj.*) misleading, deceptive; lacking in or not based on reality

Police state tactics provide an _____ sense of security in an unjust society.

SYNONYMS: specious, spurious, imaginary
ANTONYMS: actual, real, factual, objective

14. indigent
(in' də jənt)

(*adj.*) needy, impoverished

The number of homeless and _____ persons has increased since the economy took a downturn.

SYNONYMS: penniless, poverty-stricken, destitute
ANTONYMS: affluent, prosperous

15. inordinate
(in ôr' də nət)

(*adj.*) far too great, exceeding reasonable limits, excessive

The press showered the popular actor with

_____ praise for what seemed a rather ordinary performance.

SYNONYMS: exorbitant, extravagant
ANTONYMS: reasonable, equitable

16. jettison
(jet' ə sən)

(*v.*) to cast overboard, get rid of as unnecessary or burdensome

The captain ordered the crew to _____ the ballast so the ship could move more quickly through the water.

SYNONYMS: cast off, discard, dump, junk
ANTONYMS: conserve, retain, hold on to, keep

17. misanthrope
(mis' ən thrōp)

(*n.*) a person who hates or despises people

The millionaire _____ left all her money to an animal shelter and not a penny to a single human being.

SYNONYM: people-hater

18. pertinacious
(pər tə nā' shəs)

(*adj.*) very persistent; holding firmly to a course of action or a set of beliefs; hard to get rid of, refusing to be put off or denied

The defense attorney was as _____ as a bulldog in his cross-examination of the witness.

SYNONYMS: stubborn, determined

19. picayune
(pik ē yün')

(*adj.*) of little value or importance, paltry, measly; concerned with trifling matters, small-minded

A supervisor who fusses about every

_____ fault of the workers will lower morale and productivity.

SYNONYMS: piddling, trifling
ANTONYMS: important, significant, huge, gigantic

20. raiment
(rā' mənt)

(*n.*) clothing, garments

When the chorus in the Greek tragedy hears that the king has died, they tear their _____ in anguish.

SYNONYMS: apparel, attire

Choosing the Right Word

*Select the **boldface** word that better completes each sentence. You might refer to the selection on pages 88–89 to see how most of these words are used in context.*

1. Ralph Waldo Emerson and a(n) (**coterie,** effrontery) of like-minded friends led the American transcendentalism movement in the mid-nineteenth century.

2. Though the federal government does much to help the (**indigent,** illusory), private charities play no small part in their welfare.

3. To anyone as fond of horses as I am, the stable and the tack room provide as (indigent, **convivial**) an atmosphere as one could wish for.

4. I can always come up with the crushing rejoinder, the dazzling witticism, or the (furtive, **felicitous**) phrase—about an hour after I need it!

5. When I returned to the office earlier than expected, I caught the little snoop (felicitously, **furtively**) going through the papers on my desk.

In the 1840s, Ralph Waldo Emerson founded and contributed to *The Dial*, a magazine that explored transcendental philosophy.

6. The presidency is the "toughest job in the world" because it makes such (bestial, **inordinate**) demands on a person's time, energy, and ingenuity.

7. Nothing we could say seemed to (demur, **allay**) her grief over the loss of her dog.

8. If installment buying is not carefully controlled, the benefits that can accrue from it may prove wholly (**illusory,** inordinate).

9. The atrocities committed by the (garish, **bestial**) commanders of such concentration camps as Auschwitz appalled the civilized world.

10. As the rock star's popularity began to skyrocket, what had been a small (**coterie,** raiment) of admirers became an unruly mob.

11. I am flattered that you want me to chair the meeting, but I must (**demur,** embellish) on the grounds of my youth and inexperience.

12. The famous sleuth pursued his investigation with all the (**pertinacity,** conviviality) of a lion stalking its dinner.

13. The kind of (**garish,** picayune) theatrical makeup used by circus clowns is not suitable for an elegant fashion model.

14. Often the antonym of a given English word is not so much its opposite as its (embellishment, **counterpart**)—for example, *actor* and *actress*.

15. "You mean you had the (**effrontery,** demur) to ask for a raise when everyone knows you've been goofing off lately?" I asked in amazement.

16. The proofreader didn't notice any significant flaws in the writing, but he did find a few (**ephemeral, picayune**) errors in the punctuation.

17. When the facts of a matter speak so plainly for themselves, we shouldn't seek to (**embellish, jettison**) them.

18. She has neither the starry-eyed optimism of the idealist nor the mordant cynicism of the (**misanthrope, coterie**).

19. Every dynamic and successful society must be able to (**allay, jettison**) ideas and institutions that have outlived their usefulness.

20. Somehow, it depresses me to think that with the approach of winter this magnificent old tree will surrender all its leafy (**raiment, effrontery**).

21. An emotion so fickle and (**ephemeral, pertinacious**) does not deserve to be categorized as "love."

22. Not surprisingly, my sister's solemnly made commitment to daily clarinet practice for one month was (**garish, ephemeral**), lasting only five days.

23. Sadly, in our celebrity-obsessed culture, professional athletes make (**pertinacious, inordinate**) amounts of money while professional educators make little.

24. To celebrate their fiftieth anniversary, my grandfather described the (**felicitous, indigent**) choice he made to ask my grandmother for a first date.

25. Effective coaches are able to (**allay, embellish**) the doubts of their players.

Synonyms

*Choose the word from this unit that is the same or most nearly the same in meaning as the **boldface** word or expression in the phrase. Write that word on the line. Use a dictionary if necessary.*

1. the **dogged** researcher _____

2. a **clandestine** midnight meeting _____

3. willingly **abandoned** their prejudices _____

4. had the **gall** to demand an apology _____

5. prone to **fanciful** get-rich-quick schemes _____

6. condemned the militia's **depraved** behavior _____

7. a well-known **despiser of mankind** _____

8. **ornamented** with high-sounding phrases _____

9. ignore those **inconsequential** objections _____

10. the **fleeting** nature of power _____

Antonyms

*Choose the word from this unit that is most nearly opposite in meaning to the **boldface** word or expression in the phrase. Write that word on the line. Use a dictionary if necessary.*

1. their **forthright** attempt to withdraw   _____

2. **moderate** increases in profits   _____

3. the **social** inhabitants of the big cities   _____

4. a very **grim** lunch meeting   _____

5. **humane** behavior   _____

Completing the Sentence

From the words in this unit, choose the one that best completes each of the following sentences. Write the word in the space provided.

1. When Charles V retired to a Spanish monastery, he exchanged the costly ____raiment____ of a king for the simple habit of a monk.

2. Since we all agreed that the proposal seemed to offer the best solution to our problem, it was accepted without ____demur____.

3. A busy administrator in today's high-pressure business world just doesn't have time to deal with such ____picayune____ concerns as making coffee.

4. He is entitled to reasonable compensation for the damage to his car, but the demands he has made are totally ____inordinate____.

5. The man's features suddenly contorted into a(n) ____bestial____ mask, more reminiscent of a hobgoblin than a human being.

6. Jonathan Swift so came to loathe human folly, vice, and hypocrisy that he died a virtual ____misanthrope____.

7. The ____furtive____ manner in which he sidled into the room and tried to avoid being noticed actually drew attention to his presence.

8. The disastrous stock market crash of 1929 left many a wealthy speculator as ____indigent____ as the proverbial church mouse.

9. Who wouldn't have had fun among such a(n) ____convivial____ group of people?

10. The crew of the freighter ____jettisoned____ most of its cargo in a desperate effort to keep the sinking ship afloat.

11. The "Old 400" was a very small and exclusive ___coterie___ of prominent families that dominated East Coast society for decades.

12. Recent developments in that part of the world have intensified rather than ___allayed___ our fears of a renewed conflict.

13. At the Casablanca Conference in 1943, President Roosevelt and his military aides met with their British ___counterparts___ to map military strategy for the Western Allies.

14. A good deal of sad experience has taught me that my youthful hopes of getting something for nothing are entirely ___illusory___.

15. Though I don't consider myself much of a diplomat, I think I handled that delicate situation in a particularly ___felicitous___ manner.

16. "If at first you don't succeed, try, try again" seems to be the motto of that ___pertinacious___ young woman.

17. In the Victorian era, designers ___embellished___ women's dresses with all sorts of elaborate frills and flounces.

18. The ___garish___ movie palaces of an earlier era have given way to smaller theaters, decorated in a simpler, more austere style.

19. Many a now-forgotten "movie great" has discovered to his or her chagrin that fame may indeed be as ___ephemeral___ as a passing shower.

20. He had the ___effrontery___ to come into my own home to tell me what I should do to help him.

Writing: Words in Action

1. Look back at "John Lennon's Legacy" (pages 88–89). In it, the author mentions Lennon's "dream of fame" and his confidence that he would achieve it through his music. How important is fame to you? Would you include it as part of your definition of being successful or happy? Write an essay in which you explain your opinion of fame. Use at least two details from the passage and three unit words to explain your ideas.

2. Think about the power celebrities have to influence individual people as well as society as a whole. Do you think celebrities—including singers, actors, and professional athletes—should become politically active, or should they stay out of politics? In a brief essay, support your opinion with specific examples from current events, your reading (refer to pages 88–89), your media viewing, or your personal observations and experience. Write at least three paragraphs, and use three or more words from this unit.

Vocabulary in Context

Literary Text

The following excerpts are from Henry James's novels The Bostonians *and* Roderick Hudson. *Some of the words you have studied in this unit appear in* **boldface** *type. Complete each statement below the excerpt by circling the letter of the correct answer.*

1. Ransom could see for himself that the occasion was not crudely festive; there was a want of **convivial** movement, and, among most of the visitors, even of mutual recognition. (*The Bostonians*)

Convivial movement is
a. energetic
b. purposeful
c. knowledgeable
d. sociable

2. Basil Ransom wondered whether it were **effrontery** or innocence that enabled Miss Tarrant to meet with such complacency the aloofness of the elder lady. (*The Bostonians*)

Effrontery is
a. experience
b. impudence
c. serenity
d. sympathy

3. She was silent for a few minutes; then at last, "In that, then, we are better than Europe," she said. To a certain point Rowland agreed with her, but he **demurred**, to make her say more. (*Roderick Hudson*)

If you have **demurred**, you have
a. remained silent
b. asked a question
c. raised your voice
d. made an objection

Christopher Reeve stars as Mississippi lawyer Basil Ransom in the 1984 film version of James's *The Bostonians*.

4. Her daughter had come lawfully by her loveliness, but Rowland mentally made the distinction that the mother was silly and that the daughter was not. The mother had a very silly mouth—a mouth, Rowland suspected, capable of expressing an **inordinate** degree of unreason. (*Roderick Hudson*)

Something **inordinate** is NOT
a. admirable
b. necessary
c. moderate
d. predictable

5. Her mouth was large, fortunately for the principal grace of her physiognomy was her smile, which displayed itself with magnificent amplitude. Rowland, indeed, had not yet seen her smile, but something assured him that her rigid gravity had a radiant **counterpart**. (*Roderick Hudson*)

A **counterpart** is a(n)
a. authority
b. complement
c. extension
d. component

Interactive Quiz

Snap the code, or go to **vocabularyworkshop.com**

*Read the following selection, taking note of the **boldface** words and their contexts. These words are among those you will be studying in Unit 8. As you complete the exercises in this unit, it may help to refer to the way the words are used below.*

A Passage to Power

<Interview>

Whoever is Speaker of the U.S. House of Representatives sets House rules, adjudicates procedural conflicts, and strives to maintain civility during debates. The Speaker also exerts behind-the-scenes powers by appointing committee chairs and setting the timetables for legislative votes. To learn more about the post and its evolution, we asked the noted congressional scholar, Bill T. Kanoho, about one of the most powerful government posts.

Q: What are the requirements for the Speaker's job?

A: You must be at least 25 years old, a U.S. citizen for the previous seven years, and an inhabitant of the state you are to represent at the time of election.

Q: That's it?

A: That's what the Constitution requires. Another aspect of the post—it's slightly **macabre**—is that the Speaker is second in line, after the Vice President, to the presidency if the President can no longer serve.

Q: How do other representatives view the Speaker?

A: It's **irrefutable** that the House reveres its Speaker. After all, it's a very important position. Money talks: From the First Congress onwards, the Speaker always made more money than members of Congress. For example, in 2011, the Speaker was paid $223,500 and members of Congress $174,000.

Q: Was the role of the Speaker always as influential as it is today?

A: Actually, no. The first speaker, Frederick Muhlenberg of Pennsylvania, did little that would **portend** the post would ever grow in importance. It has become **saturated** with power, but I would say a **paucity** of change marked the role until the Twelfth Congress (1811–1813).

Q: Why so little change in those early years?

A: It wasn't that the Speakers were **lackadaisical**, and in fact I believe they all saw the expanding nation as a **juggernaut** on the world stage. But it seems the first Speakers wanted to **conciliate** the members, perhaps because in the early

John Boehner, Speaker of the House, 2011

days of our republic fistfights could erupt when one member refused to **recant** a position that angered another.

Q: Why did the job start to change?

A: Henry Clay of Kentucky stirred the pot when he served six nonconsecutive terms as Speaker, from 1811 through 1825, and made a **litany** of changes. The biggest were that he participated in debates, and he enforced strict rules of order to **slough** off attempts to **countermand** his efforts to raise the office to a new **echelon**.

Q: Is that when the job's scope became as powerful as it is today?

A: Well, after Clay left, the office returned to its original scope until 1880, when the Speaker's role was expanded to include being Chairman of the Committee on Rules, a power-filled position.

Q: Then what happened?

A: Maine's Thomas Brackett Reed is what happened. While serving as Speaker from 1889 to 1891, then again from 1895 to 1899, he made **arrant** and successful bids to increase the Speaker's power. The most notable change occurred when he masterminded how to prevent the minority party from using parliamentary maneuvers—that is, exploiting legal technicalities—to block majority party decisions.

Q: Is that when the post became truly powerful?

A: It's been evolving since then. However, it would be **fatuous** not to mention the post's current partisan profile: Republicans and Democrats sometimes have a hard time working together, so a powerful Speaker is needed in order to get things done. And sometimes problems in Congress are **exacerbated** by talking heads—talk show guests and politicians who talk in sound bites that tell only half the story and thus misrepresent an issue.

Q: What can the Speaker do to solve that problem?

A: He or she can be fair. Though politicians may pontificate and argue and attack others' positions, many voters fail to realize this is part of the game. These officials strike a pose to appeal to their constituents, then they get down to business. A lot of friendly **badinage** goes on in the House. Our elected officials are not about to **raze** the Capitol building. The Speaker wouldn't allow it!

Frederick Muhlenberg, circa 1790, was the first Speaker of the House and represented Pennsylvania.

iWords™

Snap the code, or go to **vocabularyworkshop.com**

Speaker Henry Clay served six nonconsecutive two-year terms as Speaker and made changes that started the post's evolution to what it is today.

Definitions

Note the spelling, pronunciation, part(s) of speech, and definition(s) of each of the following words. Then write the word in the blank spaces in the illustrative sentence(s) following. Finally, study the lists of synonyms and antonyms.

1. allege
(ə lej′)

(*v.*) to assert without proof or confirmation

The newspaper tabloid _____ that the movie star and the director were having creative differences.

SYNONYM: contend
ANTONYM: prove

2. arrant
(ar′ ənt)

(*adj.*) thoroughgoing, out-and-out; shameless, blatant

In Shakespeare's tragedy the audience sees clearly that Iago is an _____ scoundrel, but Othello is blind to his treachery.

SYNONYMS: egregious, unmitigated

3. badinage
(bad ə näzh′)

(*n.*) light and playful conversation

I enjoy the delightful _____ between stars like Spencer Tracy and Katharine Hepburn in 1940s movies.

SYNONYMS: banter, persiflage, repartee
ANTONYM: sermon

4. conciliate
(kən sil′ ē āt)

(*v.*) to overcome the distrust of, win over; to appease, pacify; to reconcile, make consistent

Because of the weakness of our army, we had to try to _____ the enemy.

SYNONYMS: mollify, propitiate
ANTONYMS: antagonize, alienate, estrange

5. countermand
(kaůn′ tər mand)

(*v.*) to cancel or reverse one order or command with another that is contrary to the first

Today's directive clearly _____ all previous instructions on how to exit the building in case of fire.

SYNONYMS: recall, revoke
ANTONYMS: reaffirm, reassert

6. echelon
(esh′ ə län)

(*n.*) one of a series of grades in an organization or field of activity; an organized military unit; a steplike formation or arrangement

Although the civil servant began in the lower _____ of government service, he rose quickly through the ranks.

SYNONYM: rank

7. exacerbate
(eg zas′ ər bāt)

(*v.*) to make more violent, severe, bitter, or painful

Shouting and name-calling are sure to
_____ any quarrel.

SYNONYMS: intensify, worsen
ANTONYMS: alleviate, mitigate, ameliorate

8. fatuous
(fach′ ü əs)

(*adj.*) stupid or foolish in a self-satisfied way

In order to discredit the candidate, the columnist quoted
some of his more _____, self-serving
remarks.

SYNONYMS: silly, vapid, inane, doltish, vacuous
ANTONYMS: intelligent, perceptive, bright

9. irrefutable
(ir i fyü′ tə bəl)

(*adj.*) impossible to disprove; beyond argument

The jury felt the prosecution presented it with
_____ evidence of the defendant's guilt.

SYNONYMS: indisputable, incontrovertible, undeniable
ANTONYMS: disputable, indefensible, untenable

10. juggernaut
(jəg′ ər nôt)

(*n.*) a massive and inescapable force or object that crushes
whatever is in its path

Any population that has experienced the
_____ of war firsthand will
not easily forget its destructive power.

11. lackadaisical
(lak ə dā′ zə kəl)

(*adj.*) lacking spirit or interest, halfhearted

The team's performance in the late innings was
_____ because they were so far ahead.

SYNONYMS: indolent, indifferent, lax
ANTONYMS: energetic, vigorous, wholehearted

12. litany
(lit′ ə nē)

(*n.*) a prayer consisting of short appeals to God recited by the
leader alternating with responses from the congregation; any
repetitive chant; a long list

Whenever she talks about her childhood, she recites an
interminable _____ of grievances.

SYNONYMS: catalog, megillah

13. macabre
(mə käb′)

(*adj.*) grisly, gruesome; horrible, distressing; having death as
a subject

The continuing popularity of horror movies suggests that
one way to score at the box office is to exploit
_____ situations.

SYNONYMS: grim, ghoulish

14. paucity
(pô′ sə tē)

(*n.*) an inadequate quantity, scarcity, dearth
The senate campaign was marred by a
_____ of original ideas.

SYNONYM: lack
ANTONYMS: glut, plenitude, deluge

15. portend
(por tənd′)

(*v.*) to indicate beforehand that something is about to happen;
to give advance warning of
In Shakespeare's plays, disturbances in the heavens usually
_____ disaster or trouble in human affairs.

SYNONYMS: bode, foretell, suggest

16. raze
(rāz)

(*v.*) to tear down, destroy completely; to cut or scrape off or out
The town _____ the old schoolhouse to
make room for a larger, more modern school complex.

SYNONYMS: pull down, demolish, shave off
ANTONYMS: build, construct, raise, erect

17. recant
(ri kant′)

(*v.*) to withdraw a statement or belief to which one has
previously been committed, renounce, retract
On the stand, the defendant _____ the
guilty admissions she had made in her confession to the
police.

SYNONYMS: repudiate, disavow
ANTONYM: reassert

18. saturate
(sach′ ə rāt)

(*v.*) to soak thoroughly, fill to capacity; to satisfy fully
A sponge that is _____ with water swells
up but does not drip.

SYNONYMS: drench, flood, imbue; ANTONYM: drain

19. saturnine
(sat′ ər nīn)

(*adj.*) of a gloomy or surly disposition; cold or sluggish in mood
Ebenezer Scrooge, of Dickens's *A Christmas Carol*, has a
decidedly _____ temperament.

SYNONYM: morose; ANTONYMS: cheerful, vivacious

20. slough
(sləf)

(*v.*) to cast off, discard; to get rid of something objectionable or
unnecessary; to plod through as if through mud; (*n.*) a mire; a
state of depression
At New Year's time, many people resolve to
_____ off bad habits and live better.
The advancing line of tanks became bogged down in a
_____ .

SYNONYMS: (*v.*) shed, slog
ANTONYMS: (*v.*) take on, acquire, assume

Choosing the Right Word

Select the **boldface** word that better completes each sentence. You might refer to the selection on pages 98–99 to see how most of these words are used in context.

1. On the Western Front in August 1914, the French army steeled itself against the oncoming (**badinage, juggernaut**) that was the German Second Army.

2. Not surprisingly, the committee's final report was an incongruous mixture of the astute and the (**irrefutable, fatuous**).

3. By (**portending, sloughing**) off the artificiality of her first book, the novelist arrived at a style that was simple, genuine, and highly effective.

4. What possible purpose will be served by setting up yet another hamburger stand in an area already (**saturated, sloughed**) with fast-food shops?

A French solider protects himself from shrapnel in a trench during World War I.

5. Our excitement at visiting the world-famous ruins was dampened by the (**lackadaisical, arrant**) attitude of the bored and listless guide.

6. The authority of the student council is not absolute because the principal can (**countermand, exacerbate**) any of its decisions.

7. It is a good deal easier to (**raze, allege**) an old building than it is to destroy a time-honored social institution.

8. I never ask anyone, "How are you?" anymore because I am afraid I will be treated to an endless (**litany, badinage**) of symptoms and ailments.

9. His debating technique is rooted in the firm belief that anything bellowed in a loud voice is absolutely (**saturnine, irrefutable**).

10. The views of the two parties involved in this dispute are so diametrically opposed that it will be almost impossible to (**conciliate, saturate**) them.

11. Only a(n) (**arrant, macabre**) knave would be capable of devising such an incredibly underhanded and treacherous scheme.

12. In earlier times, people whose views conflicted with "received opinion" often had to (**recant, portend**) their ideas or face the consequences.

13. Stephen King's book *Danse* (**Macabre, Lackadaisical**) surveys popular and obscure horror fiction of the twentieth century.

14. Over the years, hard work and unstinting devotion to duty have raised me from one (**echelon, paucity**) of company management to the next.

15. She excused herself from lending me the money I so desperately needed by (**conciliating, alleging**) that she had financial troubles of her own.

16. By denying your guilt without offering any explanation of your actions, you will only (**recant, exacerbate**) an already bad situation.

17. Economists believe that the drop in automobile sales and steel production (**countermands, portends**) serious problems for business in the future.

18. His attempts at casual (**badinage, echelon**) did not conceal the fact that he was acutely embarrassed by his blunder.

19. We have many capable and well-meaning people in our organization, but it seems to me that there is a (**paucity, juggernaut**) of real leadership.

20. Someone with such a (**fatuous, saturnine**) outlook on life doesn't make an agreeable traveling companion, especially on a long journey.

21. With incredible unconcern, the nobles of Europe immersed themselves in social frivolities as the fearful (**juggernaut, litany**) of World War I steamrolled ineluctably toward them.

22. Ever a bit of a melancholic, Mr. Smithers sank into a (**litany, slough**) in the wintertime.

23. The defense attorney succeeded in portraying the genial witness as a(n) (**arrant, saturnine**) liar, whose testimony was never credible.

24. The dog's owner (**exacerbated, razed**) the situation when he flagrantly encouraged the terrier to romp in the neighbor's petunias.

25. A plunge in atmospheric pressure (**conciliates, portends**) an oncoming storm.

Synonyms

*Choose the word from this unit that is the same or most nearly the same in meaning as the **boldface** word or expression in the phrase. Write that word on the line. Use a dictionary if necessary.*

1. seemed in a **sullen** mood _____

2. **claimed** that a crime had been committed _____

3. **foreshadows** dangers to come _____

4. an idea that **permeates** all aspects of society _____

5. will **aggravate** tensions between the rivals _____

6. a long **rigmarole** of questions and answers _____

7. a **listless** response from voters _____

8. the upper **levels** of power _____

9. tried to **placate** both sides in the dispute _____

10. wore a very **grotesque** mask _____

Antonyms

*Choose the word from this unit that is most nearly opposite in meaning to the **boldface** word or expression in the phrase. Write that word on the line. Use a dictionary if necessary.*

1. a growing **abundance** of cheap labor   _____

2. given to **lighthearted** predictions   _____

3. known for his **sensible** opinions   _____

4. has **reaffirmed** her support of free trade   _____

5. **deny** involvement in the burglary   _____

Completing the Sentence

From the words in this unit, choose the one that best completes each of the following sentences. Write the word in the space provided.

1. The breaking news story concerned corruption among the highest _____echelon_____ of politics.

2. We object to the policy of _____razing_____ historic old buildings to make way for unsightly parking lots.

3. Ms. Ryan's warnings to the class to "review thoroughly" seemed to me to _____portend_____ an unusually difficult examination.

4. The seriousness of the matter under discussion left no room for the type of lighthearted _____badinage_____ encountered in the locker room.

5. At first I thought it would be easy to shoot holes in their case, but I soon realized that their arguments were practically _____irrefutable_____.

6. As a snake _____sloughs_____ off its old skin, so he hoped to rid himself of his weaknesses and develop a new and better personality.

7. Though some "home remedies" appear to alleviate the symptoms of a disease, they may in fact _____exacerbate_____ the condition.

8. After he made that absurd remark, a(n) _____fatuous_____ grin of self-congratulation spread like syrup across his face.

9. The men now being held in police custody are _____alleged_____ to have robbed eight supermarkets over the last year.

10. Only someone with a truly _____macabre_____ sense of humor would decide to use a hearse as the family car or a coffin as a bed.

11. My shirt became so ___saturated___ with perspiration on that beastly day that I had to change it more than once during the match.

12. You are not going to do well in your job if you continue to work in such a(n) ___lackadaisical___ and desultory manner.

13. No sooner had the feckless tsar decreed a general mobilization than he ___countermand___ his order, only to reissue it a short time later.

14. Her friendly manner and disarming smile helped to ___conciliate___ those who opposed her views on the proposal.

15. The enemy's lines crumpled before the mighty ___juggernaut___ of our attack like so much wheat before a harvester.

16. "I find it terribly depressing to be around people whose dispositions are so ___saturnine___ and misanthropic," I remarked.

17. His four disastrous years in office were marked by a plenitude of promises and a(n) ___paucity___ of performance.

18. The service in honor of the miners trapped in the underground collapse included prayers and ___litanies___.

19. However much it may cost me, I will never ___recant___ the principles to which I have devoted my life.

20. "It seems to me that such ___arrant___ hypocrisy is indicative of a thoroughly opportunistic approach to running for office," I said sadly.

Writing: Words in Action

1. Look back at "A Passage to Power" (pages 98–99). Think about the three requirements for the Speaker's job—the Speaker must be at least 25 years old, a United States citizen for the previous seven years, and a resident in the state that he or she represents. In a brief essay, explain which of those three requirements you believe is the most important. Use at least two details from the passage and three unit words to support your answer.

2. *"Compromise is usually a sign of weakness, or an admission of defeat. Strong men don't compromise, it is said, and principles should never be compromised." –Andrew Carnegie*

One challenge for the Speaker is deciding if and when to compromise with other members. Do you agree with businessman Andrew Carnegie that compromise is often a sign of weakness? Would you ever compromise your principles? Write an expository essay that explains your view. Support your ideas with specific examples from your personal experience or from your studies. Write at least three paragraphs, and use three or more unit words.

Vocabulary in Context

Literary Text

The following excerpts are from William Makepeace Thackeray's novels Vanity Fair *and* The History of Henry Esmond. *Some of the words you have studied in this unit appear in* **boldface** *type. Complete each statement below the excerpt by circling the letter of the correct answer.*

1. "When she comes to tea here she does not speak a word during the whole evening. She is but a poor **lackadaisical** creature, and it is my belief has no heart at all. It is only her pretty face which all you gentlemen admire so." (*Vanity Fair*)

   Someone who is **lackadaisical** is NOT

   a. vigorous   **c.** intelligent
   b. ordinary   **d.** kind

2. And so having easily won the daughter's good-will, the indefatigable little woman bent herself to **conciliate** the august Lady Southdown. As soon as she found her Ladyship alone, Rebecca attacked her on the nursery question at once and said that her own little boy was saved, actually saved, by calomel, freely administered, when all the physicians in Paris had given the dear child up. (*Vanity Fair*)

   To **conciliate** is to

   a. exonerate   **c.** appease
   b. demean   **d.** bewilder

3. O, my dear brethren and fellow-sojourners in Vanity Fair, which among you does not know and suffer under such benevolent despots? It is in vain you say to them, "Dear Madam, I took Podgers' specific at your orders last year, and believe in it. Why, why am I to **recant** and accept the Rodgers' articles now?" (*Vanity Fair*)

   To **recant** is to

   a. renounce   **c.** apologize
   b. proclaim   **d.** sacrifice

A scene from the 2004 film version of *Vanity Fair*, starring Reese Witherspoon as Becky Sharp.

4. Although Mr. Esmond had told Jack Lockwood to get horses and they would ride for Winchester that night, when he heard this news he **countermanded** the horses at once; his business lay no longer in Hanta; all his hope and desire lay within a couple of miles of him in Kensington Park wall. (*The History of Henry Esmond*)

   Something **countermanded** is

   a. summoned   **c.** recalled
   b. restrained   **d.** scattered

5. There was a fire in the room where the cloths were drying for the baths, and there lay a heap in a corner **saturated** with the blood of my dear lord's body. Esmond went to the fire, and threw the paper into it. (*The History of Henry Esmond*)

   Something that is **saturated** is

   a. tossed carelessly   **c.** soaked completely
   b. mangled badly   **d.** stained lightly

Interactive Quiz

Snap the code, or go to **vocabularyworkshop.com**

*Read the following selection, taking note of the **boldface** words and their contexts. These words are among those you will be studying in Unit 9. As you complete the exercises in this unit, it may help to refer to the way the words are used below.*

Security Status: It's Complicated
<Persuasive Essay>

To great **acclamation**, social networking sites, websites that allow connected groups of individuals to interact online, burst onto the scene in the late 1990s. Since then, tell-all social networking sites have increased in popularity exponentially. With some sites boasting hundreds of millions of users disclosing information with total strangers and friends alike, there now exists an extensive online community sharing ideas, interests, and activities.

Social networking is, in theory, an excellent, appealing concept, but risks abound with every online **peregrination**. Sites provide ready access to personal information, so even the most **imperturbable** and experienced users must recognize and be mindful of the hazards.

Social networking sites allow users to keep in touch and build connections without much effort, but who else is effortlessly monitoring their correspondences? Corporations are, for one. Looking for market advantages, businesses use personal information to evaluate potential customers. The companies that own the social networks are, in a sense, in **collusion** with those corporations when they collect data to sell to their advertisers. But the infringements of advertisers are **paltry** problems, more **redolent** of annoying telephone marketing, than of the serious crimes committed by those who prey on social network users. For, unfortunately, along with the rapid growth of sites and their many beneficial applications, there has also emerged a veritable **paroxysm** of criminal activity associated with those sites.

Yes, there are unsavory individuals out there who are very interested in collecting the information that people post. There are identity thieves and those who **vituperatively** harass or stalk people online, or who infect computers with malware; scam artists looking to take advantage of **tyros** and veterans alike. It is another sad truth that there is a growing number of bullying teens who use social networks to cruelly **calumniate** and isolate classmates. In a few cases, cyber-bullying has led to tragedy as victims try to escape their tormentors.

Fortunately, available tools and strategies minimize risks when using social networks. Users must remain as **unremitting** in their efforts to protect their privacy as the malefactors are in theirs to breach it.

The old **shibboleth**, "Leave no stone unturned," is a **mandate** in this war against cyber criminals and against as yet unforeseen issues. Above all, users must be **chary** in what they post, providing only necessary information that errs on the side of caution and good sense. Social networkers should limit personal data in postings and provide more details in secure areas. Nobody really wants strangers to have his or her phone number or address. Remember, personal data are valuable to crooks, identity thieves, spammers, and advertisers.

Furthermore, users should familiarize themselves with a site's privacy settings and be alert to changes in them. It is a good practice to reject requests to connect with strangers looking for money. If a social network account is compromised, it should be reported to the site and the account should be closed. Protective strategies are not **pedantry**, but key components of a prudent approach to safe social networking. Social networkers must proceed with caution and common sense to enjoy the many benefits of cyber-communities.

Snap the code, or go to
vocabularyworkshop.com

Definitions

Note the spelling, pronunciation, part(s) of speech, and definition(s) of each of the following words. Then write the word in the blank spaces in the illustrative sentence(s) following. Finally, study the lists of synonyms and antonyms.

1. acclamation
(ak lə mā′ shən)

(n.) a shout of welcome; an overwhelming verbal vote of approval

It is very rare for a presidential candidate to be nominated by _____ from the convention floor.

SYNONYMS: ovation, cheering, plaudits
ANTONYMS: booing, hissing, jeers, catcalls

2. bucolic
(byü käl′ ik)

(adj.) characteristic of the countryside, rural; relating to shepherds and cowherds, pastoral

The Elizabethans who wrote of shepherds in ideal country settings were imitating the Greek _____ poets.

SYNONYM: rustic
ANTONYM: metropolitan

3. calumniate
(kə ləm′ nē āt)

(v.) to slander; to accuse falsely and maliciously

Not only did the artist's enemy seek to discredit her while she was alive but tried to _____ her memory as well.

SYNONYMS: defame, libel
ANTONYMS: flatter, whitewash, praise

4. chary
(châr′ ē)

(adj.) extremely cautious, hesitant, or slow (to); reserved, diffident

Since so many funds had been spent with so few results, they were _____ about appropriating more money.

SYNONYM: skittish
ANTONYMS: heedless, reckless, incautious

5. collusion
(kə lü′ zhən)

(n.) secret agreement or cooperation

Years later, it was discovered that senior members of the company had been in _____ with the enemy.

SYNONYMS: conspiracy, plot, connivance

6. dilettante
(dil′ ə tänt)

(n.) a dabbler in the arts; one who engages in an activity in an amateurish, trifling way; (adj.) superficial

Many people dismissed the poster artists of the 1960s as mere _____ with nothing serious to say about life or art.

SYNONYM: amateur
ANTONYM: professional

7. imperturbable
(im pər tər' bə bəl)

(*adj.*) not easily excited; emotionally steady

The witness remained _____ throughout the grueling cross-examination.

SYNONYMS: unflappable, unexcitable, serene, unruffled
ANTONYM: excitable

8. increment
(in' krə mənt)

(*n.*) an enlargement, increase, addition

Employees were added to the work force in _____ of five to reduce training costs.

SYNONYM: accretion
ANTONYMS: reduction, decrease

9. mandate
(man' dāt)

(*n.*) an authoritative command, formal order, authorization; (*v.*) to issue such an order

The peacekeepers were sent into the war-torn country under a UN _____ to protect civilians.

The environmental protection agency has _____ that all automobiles pass an annual emissions test.

SYNONYM: (*n.*) directive
ANTONYMS: (*v.*) forbid, ban, outlaw

10. paltry
(pôl' trē)

(*adj.*) trifling, insignificant; mean, despicable; inferior, trashy

The billionaire was so greedy that he contributed only a _____ sum of money to charity each year.

SYNONYMS: measly, meager, piddling, trivial
ANTONYMS: gigantic, immense

11. paroxysm
(par' ək siz əm)

(*n.*) a sudden outburst; a spasm, convulsion

The children greeted the clown with a _____ of laughter when he began making his funny faces.

SYNONYMS: fit, seizure

12. pedantry
(ped' ən trē)

(*n.*) a pretentious display of knowledge; overly rigid attention to rules and details

The fussy music professor was distinguished more for her _____ than her true scholarship.

SYNONYMS: nit-picking, pettifoggery

13. peregrination
(per ə grə nā' shən)

(*n.*) the act of traveling; an excursion, especially on foot or to a foreign country

After returning from my _____ throughout South America, I wrote a book about my experiences.

SYNONYMS: journey, wandering, odyssey

14. redolent
(red′ ə lənt)

(*adj.*) fragrant, smelling strongly; tending to arouse memories or create an aura

My grandmother's kitchen was always _____ with the smells of baking.

SYNONYMS: evocative, reminiscent, aromatic
ANTONYMS: unevocative, odorless

15. refulgent
(ri fəl′ jənt)

(*adj.*) shining, radiant, resplendent

The swift-flowing stream beside our house was _____ in the morning light.

SYNONYM: splendid
ANTONYMS: dim, dark, obscure, dingy, dull

16. shibboleth
(shib′ ə leth)

(*n.*) a word, expression, or custom that distinguishes a particular group of persons from all others; a commonplace saying or truism

By the time Election Day rolls around, most voters are tired of hearing the same old promises and

_____.

SYNONYMS: password, slogan

17. tyro
(tī′ rō)

(*n.*) a beginner, novice; one with little or no background or skill

You cannot expect a mere _____ to perform like a veteran in his first season of major league play.

SYNONYM: neophyte
ANTONYMS: veteran, past master, expert

18. unremitting
(ən ri mit′ iŋ)

(*adj.*) not stopping, maintained steadily, never letting up, relentless

The social laws in Edith Wharton's novels are

_____.

SYNONYMS: incessant, unrelenting
ANTONYMS: desultory, intermittent

19. vacillate
(vas′ ə lāt)

(*v.*) to swing indecisively from one idea or course of action to another; to waver weakly in mind or will

Someone who _____ in a crisis should not be in a position of leadership.

SYNONYMS: fluctuate, oscillate
ANTONYM: persevere

20. vituperative
(vī tü′ pər ə tiv)

(*adj.*) harshly abusive, severely scolding

That _____ speech in which she blamed others for her own mistakes may have cost her the election.

SYNONYMS: abusive, scurrilous, insulting
ANTONYMS: complimentary, laudatory, flattering

Choosing the Right Word

Select the **boldface** word that better completes each sentence. You might refer to the selection on pages 108–109 to see how most of these words are used in context.

1. Many of the most well-known paintings of Grandma Moses portray rural scenes that are (**redolent, vituperative**) of her childhood in upstate New York.

2. Because my teacher is usually so (**chary, imperturbable**) of giving compliments, I felt really good when she spoke well of my essay.

3. Isn't it sheer (**pedantry, refulgence**) on his part to use terms like *Proustian* and *Kafkaesque* when he knows they mean nothing to his audience?

4. Although he has been in this business for 20 years, he still has the sublime innocence of the most helpless (**tyro, shibboleth**).

Born in 1860, Anna Mary Robertson, better known as "Grandma Moses," began painting in her seventies.

5. Not satisfied with the slow (**increment, peregrination**) of his savings in a bank account, he turned to speculation in the stock market.

6. Are we to try to make a realistic analysis of our alternatives or let ourselves be distracted by slogans and (**tyros, shibboleths**)?

7. Once the senator's nomination became a certainty, all opposition to him evaporated, and he was named by (**vituperation, acclamation**).

8. Perhaps he would be less lyrical about the delights of the (**bucolic, redolent**) life if, like me, he had grown up on a farm in Kansas.

9. The gambler's predictions of the game scores were so incredibly accurate that we suspected some form of (**acclamation, collusion**).

10. The same difficulties that serve as a challenge to the true professional will be a crushing discouragement to the typical (**mandate, dilettante**).

11. I'm not sure if Tom's (**imperturbable, collusive**) spirit is due to toughness or to an inability to understand the dangers of the situation.

12. Since she comes from a rural area, she expresses herself in language that is (**redolent, paltry**) of the farm and of country life in general.

13. During the course of my (**peregrinations, paroxysms**) through the world of books, I have picked up all kinds of useful information.

14. Clad in the (**refulgent, dilettante**) armor of moral rectitude, he sallied forth to do battle with the forces of evil.

15. I am perfectly willing to listen to a reasonable complaint, but I will not put up with that kind of (**bucolic, vituperative**) backbiting.

16. It has long been known that some twisted and unhappy people derive a kind of satisfaction from (**calumniating, colluding**) others.

17. The phrase "We the people" in the Constitution indicates that the ultimate (**mandate, vacillation**) of our government comes from the popular will.

18. If we (**vacillate, increment**) now at adopting a tough energy policy, we may find ourselves in a desperate situation in the future.

19. How do you have the nerve to offer such a(n) (**paltry, unremitting**) sum for this magnificent "antique" car!

20. A (**paroxysm, pedantry**) of indignation flashed though the community, and the streets filled with angry people ready to protest the proposal.

21. It is easy to criticize him, but how can we overlook the fact that for 20 years he has worked (**unremittingly, charily**) to help the homeless?

22. Although Martin thinks he is an expert software developer, many of his dissatisfied clients view him as merely a (**paroxysm, tyro**).

23. The senate candidate claimed that her opponent's most recent television ad (**calumniated, vacillated**) her husband and children.

24. During our family's recent (**peregrination, acclamation**) to the New Orleans French Quarter, we attended several jazz concerts.

25. (**Paltry, Refulgent**) attendance on opening night caused a financial crisis.

Synonyms

*Choose the word from this unit that is the same or most nearly the same in meaning as the **boldface** word or expression in the phrase. Write that word on the line. Use a dictionary if necessary.*

1. large **gain** in tax revenues _____

2. in **cahoots** with the competition _____

3. kept up the **constant** pressure to surrender _____

4. a stunningly **luminous** smile _____

5. bored us with his **hairsplitting** _____

6. **seesawed** in their commitments _____

7. keeps repeating the tired old **catchphrases** _____

8. labeled a mere **trifler** by the experts _____

9. **wary** of flattery and favor-seekers _____

10. painted a charming **country** scene _____

Antonyms

*Choose the word from this unit that is most nearly opposite in meaning to the **boldface** word or expression in the phrase. Write that word on the line. Use a dictionary if necessary.*

1. a **scholar** of poetry

   _____

2. a **colossal** amount of debt

   _____

3. reported a steady **loss** in annual sales

   _____

4. felt relief that the market was able to **stabilize**

   _____

5. prefers the **urban** lifestyle

   _____

Completing the Sentence

From the words in this unit, choose the one that best completes each of the following sentences. Write the word in the space provided.

1. In a series of searing orations, filled with the most _vituperative_ language, Cicero launched the full battery of political invective against the hapless Mark Antony.

2. The scene may seem ordinary to you, but I find it _redolent_ with memories of happy summers spent in these woods.

3. As we waited through the long night for the arrival of the rescue party, we _vacillated_ between hope and despair.

4. However long and hard the struggle, we must be _unremitting_ in our efforts to wipe out racism in this country.

5. Since Lucy had expected no more than polite applause, she was delighted by the _acclamation_ she received from the audience.

6. The contractor was suspected of having acted in _collusion_ with a state official to fix the bids on certain public works contracts.

7. The painting shows a restfully _bucolic_ scene, with some cows grazing placidly in a meadow as their shepherd dozes under a bush.

8. I thought I was unexcitable, but she is as _imperturbable_ as the granite lions in front of the public library.

9. In my various _peregrinations_ through that vast metropolis, I ran across many curious old buildings that the ordinary tourist never sees.

10. It is sheer _pedantry_ to insist upon applying the rules of formal literary composition to everyday speech and writing.

11. I have learned from long experience to be extremely _chary_ about offering advice when it has not been requested.

12. The Pledge of Allegiance is no mere _shibboleth_ to be recited mechanically and without understanding like some advertising jingle.

13. She may have great musical talents, but she will get nowhere as long as she has the casual attitude of the _dilettante_.

14. Since Lincoln is now considered a great national hero, it is hard to believe that he was bitterly _calumniated_ when he was President.

15. I had expected a decent tip from the party of six that I waited on early that evening, but all I got was a(n) _paltry_ two bucks!

16. "The overwhelming victory I have won at the polls," the Governor-elect said, "has given me a clear _mandate_ to carry out my program."

17. Seized by a(n) _paroxysm_ of rage, he began to beat the bars of his cell with his bare hands.

18. Even the merest _tyro_ in the use of firearms knows that a gun should never be pointed at another person.

19. Every time I sign a new lease on my apartment, my rent goes up, though the _increments_ are not usually very large.

20. As a(n) _refulgent_ summer sun sank slowly in the west, the skies were ablaze with color.

Writing: Words in Action

1. Look back at "Security Status: It's Complicated" (pages 108–109). Suppose that you work for an organization that educates the public about the potential dangers of social networking sites. You want to write a letter to the editor that persuades parents to take steps to ensure their young children use such sites appropriately and safely. Use at least two details from the essay and three unit words in your letter.

2. Think about how the experience of communicating with somebody by phone is different from that of communicating through social networking sites. Write an essay of at least three paragraphs in which you compare and contrast telephone and computer conversations. Use examples from your reading (refer to pages 108–109), prior knowledge, and personal experience to support your points of comparison. Use three or more words from this unit.

Vocabulary in Context

Literary Text

The following excerpts are from George Eliot's novels The Mill on the Floss *and* Romola. *Some of the words you have studied in this unit appear in* **boldface** *type. Complete each statement below the excerpt by circling the letter of the correct answer.*

1. Once before, since his illness, he had had a similar **paroxysm**, in which he had beaten his horse, and the scene had left a lasting terror in Maggie's mind. The thought had risen, that some time or other he might beat her mother if she happened to speak in her feeble way at the wrong moment. (*The Mill on the Floss*)

   A **paroxysm** is a(n)

   a. convulsion
   b. disease
   c. inclination
   d. hallucination

2. "They're **paltry** times, these are. Why, mum, look at the printed cottons now, an' what they was when you wore 'em, — why you wouldn't put such a thing on now, I can see." (*The Mill on the Floss*)

   Paltry times are definitely NOT

   a. diverse
   b. memorable
   c. wealthy
   d. inevitable

3. The nineteenth of May had come, and by that day's sunshine there had entered into Florence the two Papal Commissaries, charged with the completion of Savonarola's trial. They entered amid the **acclamations** of the people, calling for the death of the Frate. (*Romola*)

   Acclamations are

   a. demands for revenge
   b. angry protests
   c. shouts of welcome
   d. frightened cries

4. "Pardon, Messer Piero," said Tito, with his **imperturbable** good-humor; "I acted without sufficient reflection. I remembered nothing but your admirable skill in inventing pretty caprices, when a sudden desire for something of that sort prompted me to come to you." (*Romola*)

   Something that is **imperturbable** is

   a. undeniable and obvious
   b. quiet and understated
   c. witty and sarcastic
   d. steady and not easily excited

5. Every day the distress became sharper: every day the murmurs became louder. And, to crown the difficulties of the government, for a month and more—in obedience to a **mandate** from Rome—Fra Girolamo had ceased to preach. *(Romola)*

   A **mandate** is a

   a. document
   b. command
   c. deliberation
   d. plea

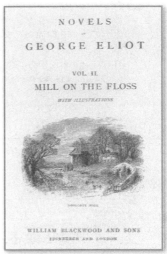

NOVELS
of
GEORGE ELIOT

VOL. II.
MILL ON THE FLOSS
WITH ILLUSTRATIONS

WILLIAM BLACKWOOD AND SONS
EDINBURGH AND LONDON

Mary Ann Evans used the pen name George Eliot when she published *The Mill on the Floss* in 1860.

Interactive Quiz

Snap the code, or go to
vocabularyworkshop.com

Vocabulary for Comprehension

*Read the following selection in which some of the words you have studied in Units 7–9 appear in **boldface** type. Then answer the questions on page 119.*

As this passage shows, the central goal of the League of Women Voters is good citizenship.

(Line)

The League of Women Voters is a citizen advocacy organization that was developed as a result of the women's suffrage movement. It was

(5) founded in 1920 by the suffragist Carrie Chapman Catt, an **unremitting** champion of women's rights and social reform. Its immediate mission was to help

(10) inform and empower the 20 million American women who were enfranchised as a result of the passage in 1920 of the Nineteenth Amendment to the U.S. Constitution.

(15) Over the years, however, the League has advocated issues less directly related to the women's movement. It has supported programs as diverse as assistance

(20) to the **indigent** during the Great Depression, civil rights in the 1960s, and environmental conservation and campaign finance reform today. Though the League vigorously

(25) champions its causes, it sees itself as staunchly nonpartisan. In other words, the League supports programs and policies but **demurs** when asked to endorse specific

(30) parties or candidates. This stance has led critics on both the left and the right to **allege** that the League is a **coterie** of activists with a hidden agenda concealed behind a banner

(35) of nonpartisanship. The League replies that it is undeniably political but definitely not partisan.

The League also takes great pride in its grassroots style of organization.

(40) Policy decisions are not made by a few leaders in the upper **echelons** of the organization, but rather are arrived at by intense study, debate, and consensus building among the

(45) rank-and-file membership at the chapter level. This reflects the League's attitude toward the power of well-informed citizens in a democracy, who ideally will make

(50) choices that will lead to a better life for all.

1. The main purpose of the first paragraph (lines 1–14) is to
   a. discuss the origins of the League
   b. explain why women had to wait so long for the vote
   c. analyze the opposition to the Nineteenth Amendment
   d. highlight the career of Carrie Chapman Catt
   e. show how the League of Women Voters got its name

2. According to the passage, the League's original mission was to
   a. advise Republican candidates in the 1920 election
   b. inform and empower newly enfranchised women voters
   c. lobby for campaign finance reform
   d. create a grassroots organization of local chapters
   e. lobby for passage of the Nineteenth Amendment

3. The meaning of **unremitting** (line 7) is
   a. controversial
   b. incomparable
   c. unrelenting
   d. undefeated
   e. intolerant

4. **Indigent** (line 20) most nearly means
   a. penniless
   b. handicapped
   c. despondent
   d. oppressed
   e. homeless

5. **Demurs** (line 28) is best defined as
   a. debates
   b. objects
   c. waffles
   d. consents
   e. rethinks

6. The meaning of **allege** (line 32) is
   a. refute
   b. imply
   c. claim
   d. deny
   e. dispute

7. **Coterie** (line 33) most nearly means
   a. conspiracy
   b. party
   c. clique
   d. family
   e. gang

8. From the details the author provides in paragraph 2 (lines 15–37), you may reasonably infer that the League has at times been
   a. undemocratic
   b. partisan
   c. unsuccessful
   d. inconsistent
   e. controversial

9. Which of the following best identifies the comparison/contrast the writer makes in paragraph 2?
   a. Republicans vs. Democrats
   b. critics on the left vs. critics on the right
   c. political vs. partisan
   d. the Great Depression vs. the Civil Rights movement
   e. national issues vs. local issues

10. The author identifies all of the following as activities of the League EXCEPT
    a. assisting the indigent
    b. supporting environmental conservation
    c. informing citizens
    d. lobbying for tax cuts
    e. advocating campaign finance reform

11. **Echelons** (line 41) most nearly means
    a. floors
    b. classes
    c. salaries
    d. offices
    e. levels

12. The author's attitude toward the League may best be described as
    a. romantic
    b. skeptical
    c. reflective
    d. hostile
    e. admiring

Two-Word Completions

Select the pair of words that best complete the meaning of each of the following passages.

1. The _____ rains had so _____ the ground over which we passed that it actually squished and gurgled in protest as we trod on it, and our attack had to be postponed until the sun came out again.
   a. inordinate . . . razed
   b. ephemeral . . . embellished
   c. unremitting . . . saturated
   d. bestial . . . jettisoned

2. In Chaucer's *Canterbury Tales*, twenty-nine travelers from various _____ of society set out for Canterbury on a pilgrimage to the shrine of Saint Thomas Beckett. At night the _____ of travelers shares its stories in order to help time pass.
   a. mandates . . . collusion
   b. litanies . . . raiment
   c. echelons . . . coterie
   d. shibboleths . . . paucity

3. Though the official is _____ to have been in cahoots with the swindlers, so far no substantive evidence has been brought forward to prove _____.
   a. portended . . . acclamation
   b. demurred . . . peregrination
   c. alleged . . . collusion
   d. calumniated . . . badinage

4. At the June 1961 summit meetings in Vienna, President John Kennedy met with his Soviet _____, Nikita Khrushchev, in an effort to deal with sources of friction between the two superpowers and _____ international fears that the so-called Cold War was heating up.
   a. counterpart . . . allay
   b. raiment . . . mandate
   c. coterie . . . exacerbate
   d. shibboleth . . . conciliate

5. The speed with which the Kaiser issued, then _____, then reissued orders during the crisis was indicative of his essentially weak and _____ personality.
   a. embellished . . . pertinacious
   b. recanted . . . imperturbable
   c. demurred . . . fatuous
   d. countermanded . . . vacillating

6. Only a thoroughgoing _____ would enjoy castigating other people's behavior in such unremittingly harsh and _____ language.
   a. pedant . . . felicitous
   b. misanthrope . . . vituperative
   c. tyro . . . arrant
   d. dilettante . . . convivial

7. The horribly _____ furnishings sent the shocked homeowner into a(n) _____ of anger.
   a. macabre . . . increment
   b. refulgent . . . slough
   c. chary . . . effrontery
   d. garish . . . paroxysm

Idioms

In "A Passage to Power" (pages 98–99), in a response to a question about the job of Speaker of the House of Representatives, the interviewee notes that Henry Clay, a previous Speaker, "stirred the pot" in several ways. The phrase "stir the pot" is an idiom that means "cause trouble" or "deliberately bring issues to the surface." The interviewee wants to convey that Clay's actions provoked thought about and changes in the Speaker's duties and power.

An **idiom** is a phrase with a figurative, not literal, meaning. Like other figures of speech, idioms create fresh images in the minds of readers or listeners. Sometimes you will be able to figure out an idiom's meaning from context clues. Other times you may need to consult an online or print dictionary to discover or verify an idiom's meaning.

Choosing the Right Idiom

Read each sentence. Use context clues to figure out the meaning of each idiom in ***boldface*** *print. Then write the letter of the definition for the idiom in the sentence.*

1. The aging band's concert tour across Europe this summer is likely to be their **swan song**. _____

2. The parade organizers worried that high wind gusts might **play havoc with** the streamers tied to the flag poles.

3. Noting that her father had worked two jobs to pay for her college education, Maria described him as the **salt of the earth**. _____

4. After our golden retriever left muddy paw prints on the kitchen floor, we worked hard to get it **spick and span** again. _____

5. Derrick's two talkative aunts hoped to arrive at the reunion early so that they would have time to **chew the fat**. _____

6. When the **well-heeled** customer took the luxury convertible for a test drive, the salesman began dreaming of a huge commission. _____

7. The news story about the protest included a photo of several local residents who are **up in arms** over the road expansion. _____

8. "Although you might not like the turnip casserole at first," Karen added, "I hope it will **grow on you** after you've had several bites." _____

9. The judge vowed not to **split hairs** when he clarifies his ruling in the tax evasion case. _____

10. "Please **lay it on the line** when you tell me what happened," Grandma told the fidgety children as she stared at her shattered crystal vase. _____

a. argue about small details

b. having plenty of money

c. have a long chat

d. a most worthy person

e. angry

f. be totally honest

g. final performance

h. ruin

i. become increasingly liked

j. neat and clean

Writing with Idioms

Find the meaning of each idiom. (Use an online or print dictionary if necessary.) Then write a sentence for each idiom.

1. on the dot

_____

2. hit pay dirt

_____

3. behind the eight ball

_____

4. scratch the surface

_____

5. on the same wavelength

_____

_____

6. with flying colors

_____

_____

7. pick up the tab

_____

_____

8. home free

_____

9. on the table

_____

10. neither here nor there

_____

11. hem and haw

_____

12. play fast and loose with

_____

Denotation and Connotation

A dictionary provides the objective meaning of a word, its **denotation**. A word's **connotation** is its subjective meaning, which includes the emotional and implied meanings associated with the word. Connotations can be *positive*, *neutral*, or *negative*.

Suppose you were writing an essay about a famous historical figure. To convey your esteem for the person's determination, you might use words like *tenacious* or *resolute*. To suggest an excessive inflexibility, you might choose words like *obstinate* or *peremptory*.

Consider these synonyms for the neutral word *chary*:

　　　prudent　　　*circumspect*　　　*calculating*　　　*diffident*

Prudent and *circumspect* have positive connotations, whereas *calculating* and *diffident* have negative connotations.

> **Think:** Successful financial advisers are prudent and circumspect in giving advice, but calculating or diffident advisers consider their own self-interest or are overly cautious.

Look at these examples of words that are similar in denotation but have different connotations.

NEUTRAL	POSITIVE	NEGATIVE
approachable	convivial	boisterous
nerve	aplomb	effrontery
meager	streamlined	paltry

A single word may have different connotations in different contexts. For example, *family* may have a neutral connotation when it identifies a category in a biology textbook but a positive connotation when it describes loving relatives in a memoir.

Shades of Meaning

Write a plus sign (+) in the box if the word has a positive connotation. Write a minus sign (–) if the word has a negative connotation. Put a zero (0) if the word is neutral.

1. calumniate ☐　　**2.** refulgent ☐　　**3.** shibboleth ☐　　**4.** vacillate ☐

5. portend ☐　　**6.** exacerbate ☐　　**7.** bestial ☐　　**8.** embellish ☐

9. fatuous ☐　　**10.** furtive ☐　　**11.** raiment ☐　　**12.** saturnine ☐

13. mandate ☐　　**14.** indigent ☐　　**15.** felicitous ☐　　**16.** paucity ☐

Expressing the Connotation

Read each sentence. Select the word in parentheses that expresses the connotation (positive, negative, or neutral) given at the beginning of the sentence.

negative   **1.** The fairgrounds surrounding the roller coaster rides were (**redolent, odorous**) with the smells of the nearby food tents.

positive   **2.** After Officer Ramirez (**alleged, verified**) that the vehicle had been traveling 65 mph, the driver reluctantly admitted to speeding.

neutral   **3.** The arrival of Kenny and his (**coterie, mob**) of friends did not disrupt the other passengers on the plane.

negative   **4.** The mayor's relentless focus on making (**unimportant, picayune**) changes to the bill's wording frustrated the council members.

negative   **5.** On their course evaluations, students frequently complained about the pompous professor's (**pedantry, proficiency**) during lectures.

neutral   **6.** Minutes after the storms began, the white linen tablecloth became (**saturated, discolored**) with water.

neutral   **7.** The army veteran acknowledged the (**acclamation, reception**) from the audience with a nod of her head and a salute.

positive   **8.** Everyone in our family likes to discuss my (**intense, inordinate**) interest in cars and motorcycles.

Challenge: Using Connotation

Choose vocabulary words from Units 7–9 to replace the highlighted words in the sentences below. Then explain how the connotation of the replacement word changes the tone of the sentence.

badinage	litany	slough
garish	peregrination	vituperative

1. When the actress first saw her costume, she thought that the dress and coat were extremely **bright** _____.

_____

_____

2. The hikers were surprised that the marked trail took them so close to a large **meadow** _____.

_____

_____

3. Upon returning home after her blind date, Anna regaled her roommates with details of the **discussion** _____ she had with her date.

_____

_____

Classical Roots

clam, claim—to cry out, shout, call

The root *clam* appears in **acclamation** (page 110). The literal meaning of acclamation is "shouting at," but it now suggests "applause" or "an overwhelmingly favorable oral vote." Some other words based on the same root are listed below.

acclaim	clamorous	disclaimer	proclamation
claimant	declaim	irreclaimable	reclamation

From the list of words above, choose the one that corresponds to each of the brief definitions below. Write the word in the blank space in the illustrative sentence below the definition. Use an online or print dictionary if necessary.

1. a denial or disavowal of responsibility or connection; a formal refusal of one's rights or claims

   The manufacturer issued a swift _____ after mediocre reviews of its new product.

2. to applaud; to indicate strong approval; noisy and enthusiastic applause

   The winning team enjoyed vigorous public _____ in a ticker-tape parade.

3. to speak like an orator; to recite in public, make a public speech; to speak bitterly against

   The actor would _____ lines from Shakespeare in response to any comment.

4. incapable of being reformed; incapable of being rendered useful

   That region of the park is nothing more than _____ swampland.

5. an official or formal public announcement

   The clerk posted the latest mayoral _____ at the entrance to City Hall.

6. the act of bringing back or restoring to a normal or useful condition (*"to call back"*)

   Innovative irrigation techniques have resulted in the _____ of much of the desert.

7. marked by loud confusion or outcry; noisily insistent (*"crying out"*)

   The protesters outside the White House made _____ demands for reform.

8. a person who asserts a right or title

   After many years, the estranged son resurfaced as the last _____ to the estate.

*Read the following selection, taking note of the **boldface** words and their contexts. These words are among those you will be studying in Unit 10. As you complete the exercises in this unit, it may help to refer to the way the words are used below.*

What Happened to the Franklin Expedition?

<Magazine Article>

By Simon Devoucoux

The tragic story of the Franklin Expedition began promisingly enough. In 1845, Sir John Franklin and his crew of about 130 set sail with great fanfare from England to the Arctic Ocean to find the fabled Northwest Passage. Franklin, a seasoned Polar explorer, was charged with **reconnoitering** the island mazes and channels of Arctic Canada in search of a route that linked the North Atlantic to the Pacific, a transit that could save many arduous months at sea for ships traveling to the other side of the world. That was the last time Franklin and his men would ever see home, and the expedition is known as one of the most disastrous in history.

Although the expedition was **fraught** with potential dangers, the British Admiralty believed it had planned for all exigencies and addressed all **foibles** that might weaken the expedition. It commissioned

two warships, the HMS *Erebus* and HMS *Terror*, both refitted for navigating treacherous ice floes. Each vessel carried provisions for three years—including 2,500 pounds of tea and 9,000 pounds of chocolate!—and each had thousands of books. The officers and crew were clearly not required to **forgo** luxury onboard.

Although the expedition was well stocked, the Royal Navy had not fully reckoned with subzero temperatures and hazardous Arctic conditions. Officers and crew were outfitted in traditional navy uniforms, skimpy outerwear, and woolen gloves—the navy looked **askance** at changes to convention in clothing. It proved impossible for them to adapt to their new environment as the indigenous

Sir John Franklin led the lost Franklin Expedition, one of the great unsolved mysteries of the nineteenth century.

people, the Inuit, had over centuries. The Inuit, hunter-gatherers who relied on dog sleds for transportation and animal skins for warmth, had become **inured** to the formidable cold.

Before long, the two ships were irrevocably trapped in pack ice. The expedition lay in **shambles**. Franklin perished in 1847, according to notes later found by search teams, and starvation, scurvy and lead poisoning from tinned food **decimated** the crew. Under the **luminous** northern lights, more and more fell victim to disease, hypothermia, and exposure. With their ranks **attenuated**, some of the crew set out on foot to try to reach an outpost of the Hudson Bay Company, but fate was not **benign**, and the crew members died before reaching the outpost.

Three years after the doomed expedition set out, there was still no word. How could the pride of the Royal Navy disappear without a trace? The country mourned Franklin—explorers and adventurers were national heros and the attention given them by the public bordered on **obsequious**. Lady Jane Franklin campaigned vigorously for search parties to locate her husband and his ships. A reward was offered, and scores of British and American vessels set sail for the unforgiving North. What they eventually found was unsettling: a few graves, disturbing notes that made little sense, then skeletons and a trail of more than 1,000 artifacts, from sextants to silver utensils to Bibles—even some novels. But a string of facts does not add up to the truth.

Newspapers of the day referred to it as the "awful mystery," and the fate of the Franklin Expedition still intrigues us—Franklin was an experienced explorer, not a **charlatan**, and previous expeditions had been trapped in pack ice and survived, so why did his entire crew perish? **Sporadic** attempts are made today to retrace the expedition, locate the two famous shipwrecks, and uncover what really happened to Franklin and his men. But the full truth may lie submerged somewhere in the frozen depths, where it continues to **rebuff** attempts to uncover it.

Simon Devoucoux lives in Newfoundland. He is a regular contributor to Victorian Exploration Quarterly.

Snap the code, or go to
vocabularyworkshop.com

Definitions

Note the spelling, pronunciation, part(s) of speech, and definition(s) of each of the following words. Then write the word in the blank spaces in the illustrative sentence(s) following. Finally, study the lists of synonyms and antonyms.

1. askance
(ə skans')

(*adv.*) with suspicion, distrust, or disapproval

The English teacher looked _____ at the suggestion that students read compendiums of Dickens's novels.

SYNONYMS: distrustfully, suspiciously

2. attenuate
(ə ten' yü āt)

(*v.*) to make thin or slender; to weaken or lessen in force, intensity, or value

After making sure the wound was clean, the doctor took steps to _____ the victim's pain.

SYNONYMS: thin out, dilute, water down
ANTONYMS: thicken, strengthen, bolster

3. benign
(bi nīn')

(*adj.*) gentle, kind; forgiving, understanding; having a favorable or beneficial effect; not malignant

Abraham Lincoln's sensitive stepmother had a _____ influence on the lonely boy who had lost his mother.

SYNONYMS: benevolent, salubrious, harmless
ANTONYMS: malevolent, deleterious

4. cavil
(kav' əl)

(*v.*) to find fault in a petty way, carp; (*n.*) a trivial objection or criticism

I suggest you do not _____ over small things but instead focus on what is important.
Despite a few _____ I might make, I still find her to be an excellent poet.

SYNONYM: (*v.*) nitpick

5. charlatan
(shär' lə tən)

(*n.*) one who feigns knowledge or ability; a pretender, impostor, or quack

The reporter exposed the real estate agent as a _____ who routinely deceived her customers.

SYNONYM: mountebank

6. decimate
(des' ə māt)

(*v.*) to kill or destroy a large part of

Again and again, Napoleon was able to _____ the armies of his enemies and lead his men to further victories.

SYNONYM: devastate

7. foible
(foi′ bəl)

(*n.*) a weak point, failing, minor flaw

Backbiting is one human _____ not likely to be eradicated.

SYNONYMS: shortcoming, quirk
ANTONYMS: forte, virtue

8. forgo
(fôr go′)

(*v.*) to do without, abstain from, give up

One of the best, if not the easiest, ways to lose weight is to _____ dessert.

SYNONYMS: refrain from, renounce
ANTONYMS: indulge in, partake of

9. fraught
(frôt)

(*adj.*) full of or loaded with; accompanied by

Even with the most advanced equipment, expeditions to the top of Mt. Everest are still _____ with danger.

SYNONYM: charged with
ANTONYMS: devoid of, lacking, deficient in

10. inure
(in yür′)

(*v.*) to toughen, harden; to render used to something by long subjection or exposure

The Inuit have become _____ to the hardships of the long Arctic winters through years of experience.

SYNONYMS: accustom, acclimate

11. luminous
(lü′ mə nəs)

(*adj.*) emitting or reflecting light, glowing; illuminating

Walking under that _____ night sky induced in me weighty thoughts not often pondered.

SYNONYMS: bright, refulgent, lustrous
ANTONYMS: dark, opaque, dim, murky

12. obsequious
(əb sē′ kwē əs)

(*adj.*) marked by slavish attentiveness; excessively submissive, often for purely self-interested reasons

Jane Austen ridiculed characters who were _____ to the aristocracy but condescending to their social inferiors.

SYNONYMS: fawning, servile, sycophantic, mealymouthed
ANTONYMS: assertive, bumptious, candid, frank, independent

13. obtuse
(äb tüs′)

(*adj.*) blunt, not coming to a point; slow or dull in understanding; measuring between 90° and 180°; not causing a sharp impression

The lieutenant was too _____ to see the danger and led his company right into the hands of the enemy.

SYNONYMS: dumb, thick, mild, dull-witted
ANTONYMS: perceptive, quick-witted

14. oscillate
(äs' ə lāt)

(v.) to swing back and forth with a steady rhythm; to fluctuate or waver

The terrified narrator in Poe's story "The Pit and the Pendulum" watches the dreaded instrument _____ as it slowly moves toward him.

SYNONYM: vibrate

15. penitent
(pen' ə tənt)

(adj.) regretful for one's sins or mistakes; (n.) one who is sorry for wrongdoing

The thief was sincerely _____.

In the Middle Ages, _____ often confessed their sins publicly and were publicly punished.

SYNONYMS: (adj.) remorseful, regretful, rueful
ANTONYM: (adj.) remorseless

16. peremptory
(pə remp' tə rē)

(adj.) having the nature of a command that leaves no opportunity for debate, denial, or refusal; offensively self-assured, dictatorial; determined, resolute

The board members resented the director's _____ tone of voice.

SYNONYM: unconditional; ANTONYMS: irresolute, mild, unassuming

17. rebuff
(ri bəf')

(v.) to snub; to repel, drive away; (n.) a curt rejection, a check

The old man _____ his neighbors by refusing all offers of friendship.

Her _____ of my invitation was quite rude.

SYNONYMS: (v.) repulse, reject; (n.) setback
ANTONYMS: (v.) accept, welcome

18. reconnoiter
(rē kə noit' ər)

(v.) to engage in reconnaissance; to make a preliminary inspection

Infantry officers often ask for volunteers to _____ the terrain ahead before ordering their soldiers to advance.

SYNONYM: scout

19. shambles
(sham' bəlz)

(n.) a slaughterhouse; a place of mass bloodshed; a state of complete disorder and confusion, mess

The burglars made a complete _____ of the apartment in their search for money and jewelry.

20. sporadic
(spô rad' ik)

(adj.) occurring at irregular intervals, having no set plan or order

The soldiers heard _____ gunfire from the other side of the river.

SYNONYMS: intermittent, spasmodic
ANTONYMS: steady, continuous, uninterrupted

Choosing the Right Word

Select the **boldface** word that better completes each sentence. You might refer to the selection on pages 126–127 to see how most of these words are used in context.

1. A grandfather clock works by gravity; when the pendulum (**oscillates,** reconnoiters), it moves a system of weights attached to the clock's hands.

2. At an autocrat's court, free speech is usually replaced by the (penitent, **obsequious**) twaddle of flunkies and toadies.

3. We believe that classes taught by teachers with specialized training will have a (sporadic, **benign**) effect on the troubled children.

4. Though I admire the woman's strong points, I find her (rebuffs, **foibles**) comic.

5. Over the years, her (**luminous,** obtuse) descriptions and scintillating wit have helped her students master the difficult subject she taught.

6. Since he didn't want to give me credit for having done a good job, he took refuge in endless (foibles, **cavils**) about my work.

Galileo discovered that a pendulum could be used to keep time and developed the first plans for what is now known as a grandfather clock.

7. Though the small nation was always ready to settle a conflict peacefully, it was not afraid to use (luminous, **peremptory**) force when necessary.

8. We must never allow our passion for justice to be (inured, **attenuated**) to mere halfhearted goodwill.

9. I have learned that (**sporadic,** peremptory) sessions of intense "cramming" can never take the place of a regular study program.

10. Somehow or other, a bull got into the china shop and turned it into a complete (**shambles,** foibles).

11. Since he is not guided by firm principles, he (attenuates, **oscillates**) between the rival factions, looking for support from both of them.

12. During the Civil War the ranks of both armies were (**decimated,** rebuffed) as much by disease as by enemy action.

13. When I found that people I admired were looking (**askance,** sporadic) at my unconventional clothing, I resolved to remedy the situation.

14. The (decimated, **penitent**) youths agreed to work without pay until they could make restitution for the damage their carelessness had caused.

15. How could you have the heart to (**rebuff,** cavil) those people's piteous appeals for aid?

16. Even though my experiences in battle have (**inured,** caviled) me to scenes of suffering, I was horrified by the devastation wrought by the tornado.

17. Their relationship has been so (fraught, **benign**) with strife and malice that I don't see how they can ever patch things up.

18. All angles are classified as acute, right, (**obtuse,** benign), or straight, according to the number of degrees they contain.

19. Imagine the general disappointment when the so-called "miracle cure" was exposed as a fraud promoted by a (**charlatan,** cavil).

20. Bank robbers often spend a good deal of time (**reconnoitering,** rebuffing) the neighborhood where the bank they intend to rob is located.

21. Do you want to be a ballet dancer enough to (**oscillate, forgo**) all other activities?

22. Although the judge offered two minor (**shambles, cavils**) about our choreography, our dance troupe won first place in the competition.

23. The play featured the stereotypical (**obsequious, fraught**) butler who treated his employer's family with excessive and artificial politeness.

24. Was it Juan's gentle stroking of the frightened dog's neck that produced a (**benign, peremptory**) change in the animal's mood?

25. The (**penitent, obtuse**) young woman begged her mother for forgiveness.

Synonyms

*Choose the word from this unit that is the same or most nearly the same in meaning as the **boldface** word or expression in the phrase. Write that word on the line. Use a dictionary if necessary.*

1. **quibble** over who is at fault _____

2. exposed him as a complete **fraud** _____

3. a **salutary** effect on consumer confidence _____

4. **vacillated** between two choices _____

5. looked **skeptically** at their proposals _____

6. feeling **sorry** about the decision _____

7. willing to overlook its **defects** _____

8. will **spurn** his offer of marriage _____

9. his **high-handed** challenge to our authority _____

10. embarrassed by his **stupid** questions _____

Antonyms

*Choose the word from this unit that is most nearly opposite in meaning to the **boldface** word or expression in the phrase. Write that word on the line. Use a dictionary if necessary.*

1. a **tentative** request for money _____
2. set the fan to **stay still** _____
3. her **acute** handling of the issue _____
4. an entirely **unrepentant** gambler and thief _____
5. prone to **praise** unnecessarily _____

Completing the Sentence

From the words in this unit, choose the one that best completes each of the following sentences. Write the word in the space provided.

1. Although there had been some _Sporadic_ fighting earlier, the real battles of the Civil War did not begin until Bull Run in July 1861.

2. Although the moon appears to be a(n) _luminous_ body, the fact is that it only reflects light from the sun.

3. Life on the family farm has _inured_ me to hard physical labor and long hours of unremitting toil.

4. I was relieved to learn that the officials were _benign_ and that I would only have to pay a small fine.

5. During imperial times, the Roman Senate was little more than a collection of _obsequious_ yes-men, intent upon preserving their own lives by gratifying the emperor's every whim.

6. No doubt he's very sorry he got caught, but that does not mean that he's at all _penitent_ about what he did.

7. I was totally taken aback when they _rebuffed_ my kind offers of assistance so rudely and nastily.

8. During the fourteenth century, the Black Death suddenly swept across Europe, _decimating_ the population and paralyzing everyday life.

9. His statements have been so uniformly _obtuse_ that I get the impression that he is wearing a permanent pair of mental blinders.

10. Though my childhood recollections have been _attenuated_ by the passage of time, they have not been totally effaced from my memory.

11. We look ___askance___ at any program that makes it harder for city dwellers to get out and enjoy the beauties of nature.

12. The general sent scouts on ahead of the army to ___reconnoiter___ the area for a suitable site to pitch camp.

13. Good supervisors know that they can get more cooperation from their staff by making polite requests than by issuing ___peremptory___ orders.

14. Any "investment counselor" who promises to double your money overnight must be regarded as a(n) ___charlatan___ or a crook.

15. Unless the title Special Aide to the Assistant Section Manager involves a salary increase, I would just as soon ___forgo___ it.

16. The man's personality was a strange mixture of strengths and weaknesses, fortes and ___foibles___.

17. In a typical James Bond movie, Agent 007 has a series of adventures that are ___fraught___ with tongue-in-cheek peril.

18. As all kinds of wild rumors ran rampant through the besieged city, the mood of the populace ___oscillated___ between hope and despair.

19. The riot converted the quiet streets of that suburban community into a ghastly ___shambles___.

20. Though critics ___cavil___ at minor faults in the new Broadway show, the general public loved it.

Writing: Words in Action

1. Look back at "What Happened to the Franklin Expedition?" (pages 126–127). Suppose that it is 1845 and you are a member of Franklin's crew. You want to write a letter to your family members explaining the goal of the expedition and letting them know how you feel as you depart England. Use at least two details from the passage and three unit words in your explanation.

2. "The World is a book, and those who do not travel read only a page."
—Saint Augustine

Do you agree with Saint Augustine's statement? What is your view on the importance of traveling? Write a brief essay in which you develop your point of view about the value of travel. Support your position with specific examples from your reading (refer to pages 126–127), studies, experiences, or observations. Write at least three paragraphs, and use three or more words from this unit.

Vocabulary in Context

Literary Text

The following excerpts are from E.M. Forster's novels Howards End *and* A Room with a View. *Some of the words you have studied in this unit appear in* **boldface** *type. Complete each statement below the excerpt by circling the letter of the correct answer.*

1. Only in legend does the sinner come forth **penitent**, but terrible, to conquer pure woman by his resistless power. Henry was anxious to be terrible, but had not got it in him. He was a good average Englishman, who had slipped. (*Howards End*)

   A **penitent** person
   a. appears to be confident
   b. is sorry for wrongdoing
   c. shows strength
   d. seems worried

2. It pleased Margaret to hear her brother and sister talking. They did not get on overwell as a rule. For a few moments she listened to them, feeling elderly and **benign**. (*Howards End*)

   If you feel **benign**, you feel
   a. forgiving
   b. invincible
   c. dutiful
   d. sentimental

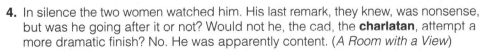

3. Margaret had given instructions that no one who mentioned her name should ever be **rebuffed**. Putting the door on the chain— for Leonard's appearance demanded this —she went through to the smoking-room, which was occupied by Tibby. (*Howards End*)

   Someone who is **rebuffed** is
   a. interrogated
   b. ignored
   c. snubbed
   d. detained

A scene from the 1985 film version of *A Room with a View*, with Julian Sands as George Emerson and Helena Bonham Carter as Lucy Honeychurch.

4. In silence the two women watched him. His last remark, they knew, was nonsense, but was he going after it or not? Would not he, the cad, the **charlatan**, attempt a more dramatic finish? No. He was apparently content. (*A Room with a View*)

   A **charlatan** is a(n)
   a. intellectual
   b. snob
   c. impostor
   d. aristocrat

5. Mrs. Honeychurch had been civil, but **obtuse** in essentials, while as for Freddy—"He is only a boy," he reflected. "I represent all that he despises. Why should he want me for a brother-in-law?" (*A Room with a View*)

   An **obtuse** person is NOT
   a. optimistic
   b. remorseful
   c. decisive
   d. perceptive

Interactive Quiz

Snap the code, or go to
vocabularyworkshop.com

*Read the following selection, taking note of the **boldface** words and their contexts. These words are among those you will be studying in Unit 11. As you complete the exercises in this unit, it may help to refer to the way the words are used below.*

Apollo 11 Poised for Take-Off

<Press Release>

For Immediate Release

Tomorrow, July 16, 1969, will mark the beginning of a bold new phase in humankind's **inexorable** quest to explore the universe. At approximately 9:30 a.m. EST, the Apollo 11 spacecraft will lift off from Cape Kennedy, Florida, for an eight-day, round-trip journey to the moon. The climax of this flight will come on July 20, when a manned lunar module will descend to the moon's surface. For the first time in history, humans will walk on another celestial body. The astronauts will explore the moon and gather rocks, dust, and other celestial **detritus** for analysis.

This mission represents the fulfillment of a universal dream. Throughout history, in every time and place, humans have stared at the moon and wondered. Wizards and **necromancers** of the past have claimed to have traveled to the moon, and storytellers and novelists have shared **delectable** tales of imaginary lunar adventures. In the past, these trips were, at best, mere flights of fancy. Today, in the shadow of the six-million-ton Saturn rocket poised for take-off, such imaginings pale and become **flaccid**, for America's astronauts will embark on a real adventure more gripping than any fiction.

The Apollo 11 mission is a response to a specific challenge. Eight years ago, President John F. Kennedy challenged the United States to land a man on the moon by the end of the decade. Such an achievement would require Americans to adopt a new and ambitious scientific outlook, discarding old and **moribund** attitudes. A few critics **deprecated** the

President's challenge, saying the nation should focus on achievements closer to home. Others saw the task, rife with problems and danger, as too **onerous**. The program's expense also was at issue: Would the cost of a program culminating in a moon landing, estimated at some $25 billion, leave the United States **impecunious**? Despite these concerns and the **asperity** of the President's response to naysayers, the majority of Americans rose to the challenge, realizing that a lunar landing would open the door to "the last frontier." In spirit, the entire nation would be going to the moon along with its astronauts.

For its part, the National Aeronautics and Space Administration (NASA) has never considered **abrogating** its commitment to a lunar landing. By mastering the **rudiments** of manned space flight during the early Mercury and Gemini flights and by learning the lessons of recent Apollo missions, NASA scientists have developed a deep and **eclectic** set of aerospace engineering skills. These have enabled NASA to construct the most complex and sophisticated equipment on earth, and thanks to these tools the agency is **ebullient** about the prospects of tomorrow's extraordinary mission. The astronauts themselves—Neil Armstrong, Michael Collins, and Edwin "Buzz" Aldrin—are also cause for optimism. To select the three candidates, NASA **winnowed** a list of thousands of the country's best pilots and aeronautical engineers. Furthermore, these three men have undergone months of intense training for the upcoming mission, **burnishing** their considerable talents and skills. Tonight they are **sequestered** near the Florida launch site, confidently awaiting their chance to make history.

Although tomorrow's thunderous takeoff will begin a journey of more than 400,000 miles, it reminds us that even a journey of one thousand miles begins with a single step. Indeed, the Apollo 11 flight is but the beginning of a much longer voyage for humankind. The question of where our scientific explorations will take us—whether to Mars, to Venus, or to other solar systems—will not be answered for many years. Undoubtedly such destinations will be on future itineraries, but as tomorrow's launch reminds us, science's ultimate destination is limited only by mankind's knowledge, individual courage, and the forces of our expanding universe.

The Apollo 11 crew: Neil Armstrong, Michael Collins, Edwin "Buzz" Aldrin

Apollo 11 ready to take off

Snap the code, or go to vocabularyworkshop.com

Definitions

Note the spelling, pronunciation, part(s) of speech, and definition(s) of each of the following words. Then write the word in the blank spaces in the illustrative sentence(s) following. Finally, study the lists of synonyms and antonyms.

1. abrogate
(ab′ rə gāt)

(*v.*) to repeal, cancel, declare null and void

Often with no legal or moral grounds, the U.S. government would _____ treaties made with Native Americans.

SYNONYMS: annul, revoke
ANTONYMS: renew, ratify

2. ambient
(am′ bē ənt)

(*adj.*) completely surrounding, encompassing

The new filtering system is capable of cleaning and deodorizing the _____ air.

3. asperity
(a sper′ ə tē)

(*n.*) roughness, severity; bitterness or tartness

The _____ of the drama critic's statements undermined the young actor's confidence.

SYNONYMS: rigor, harshness
ANTONYMS: mildness, blandness, softness, lenience

4. burnish
(bər′ nish)

(*v.*) to make smooth or glossy by rubbing, polish; (*n.*) gloss, brightness, luster

The hotel manager ordered the waiters to _____ all the brass candlesticks before the formal banquet.

The _____ on the metal frame had faded with age and neglect.

SYNONYMS: (*v.*) shine, buff
ANTONYMS: (*v.*) dull, abrade

5. cabal
(kə bäl′)

(*n.*) a small group working in secret

The members of the _____ met at an unknown location for the purpose of fixing prices and stifling competition.

SYNONYMS: ring, gang, plot, conspiracy

6. delectable
(di lek′ tə bəl)

(*adj.*) delightful, highly enjoyable; deliciously flavored, savory; (*n.*) an appealing or appetizing food or dish

The banquet ended with a truly _____ dessert made of peaches, raspberries, and ice cream.

The catery attracted customers with a mouth-watering display of _____ in its front window.

SYNONYM: (*adj.*) scrumptious
ANTONYMS: (*adj.*) repugnant, repulsive, distasteful

7. deprecate
(dep′ rə kāt)

(v.) to express mild disapproval; to belittle

The administration _____ such foolish
practices as the hazing of new students.

SYNONYMS: deplore, frown upon
ANTONYMS: smile on, approve

8. detritus
(di trīt′ əs)

(n.) loose bits and pieces of material resulting from disintegration or
wearing away; fragments that result from any destruction

Pieces of people's homes, furniture, and toys could be seen in
the _____ of the landslide.

SYNONYMS: wreckage, ruins, rubble

9. ebullient
(i bŭl′ yənt)

(adj.) overflowing with enthusiasm and excitement; boiling,
bubbling

After a string of very favorable reviews, the dance company
was in an _____ mood for weeks.

SYNONYMS: exhilarated, elated
ANTONYMS: gloomy, morose, sullen, apathetic, blasé

10. eclectic
(e klek′ tik)

(adj.) drawn from different sources; (n.) one whose beliefs are
drawn from various sources

Stanford White developed an _____ style of
architecture that made use of classic and modern elements.

The critics accused the composer of being a mere
_____ with no original style of her own.

SYNONYMS: (adj.) selective, synthetic, pick-and-choose
ANTONYMS: (adj.) uniform, monolithic

11. flaccid
(flas′ əd)

(adj.) limp, not firm; lacking vigor or effectiveness

Because the injured bodybuilder had not worked out for weeks,
his muscles grew _____.

SYNONYMS: soft, flabby; ANTONYMS: hard, solid

12. impecunious
(im pə kyü′ nē
əs)

(adj.) having little or no money

In my present _____ state, I will not be able to
pay for dinner.

SYNONYMS: impoverished, indigent
ANTONYMS: affluent, wealthy, prosperous, rich

13. inexorable
(in ek′ sər ə bəl)

(adj.) inflexible, beyond influence; relentless, unyielding

In the Greek tragedies, nothing could save characters like
Oedipus Rex from their _____ fates.

SYNONYMS: ineluctable, obdurate
ANTONYMS: avoidable, yielding, pliant

14. moribund
(môr' ə bənd)

(*adj.*) dying, on the way out

In the age of electronic communication, writing letters by hand seems to be a _____ custom.

SYNONYM: obsolescent; ANTONYM: thriving

15. necromancer
(nek' rə man sər)

(*n.*) one who claims to reveal or influence the future through magic, especially communication with the dead; in general, a magician or wizard

When the stock market began to tumble, some desperate investors resorted to _____ for financial advice.

SYNONYMS: sorcerer, conjurer

16. onerous
(än' ər əs)

(*adj.*) burdensome; involving hardship or difficulty

Informing patients of bad news is an _____ duty that every doctor has to perform.

SYNONYM: weighty; ANTONYMS: light, easy, undemanding, untaxing

17. rife
(rīf)

(*adj.*) common, prevalent, widespread, happening often; full, abounding; plentiful, abundant, replete

Since rumors were _____, the president announced that the company had been bought out by its major competitor.

ANTONYMS: devoid of, lacking

18. rudiments
(rüd' ə mənts)

(*n. pl.*) the parts of any subject or discipline that are learned first; the earliest stages of anything

At a very young age, the girl learned the _____ of chess from her father, a professional player.

SYNONYMS: basics, fundamentals

19. sequester
(si kwes' tər)

(*v.*) to set apart, separate for a special purpose; to take possession of and hold in custody

The parties agreed to _____ the disputed funds pending a decision by the court.

SYNONYMS: segregate, isolate, closet

20. winnow
(win' ō)

(*v.*) to get rid of something unwanted, delete; to sift through to obtain what is desirable; to remove the chaff from the wheat by blowing air on it; to blow on, fan

Spelling and grammar software programs are designed to help writers _____ inaccuracies from their documents.

SYNONYMS: sift, strain, filter, sort

Choosing the Right Word

*Select the **boldface** word that better completes each sentence. You might refer to the selection on pages 136–137 to see how most of these words are used in context.*

1. Oliver Wendell Holmes, Jr., once observed that he did not wish to lead a(n) (**sequestered, abrogated**) life far from the conflicts of his times.

2. Though she entered this country as a(n) (**impecunious, rife**) child, she eventually made a fortune in the garment industry.

3. "The (**inexorable, moribund**) march of the years," said the aged speaker, "decrees that this is the last time I will address you."

4. The old adage that "one man's meat is another man's poison" simply means that what is considered (**delectable, onerous**) is often quite subjective.

Oliver Wendell Holmes, Jr., was appointed to the U.S. Supreme Court in 1902 by President Theodore Roosevelt.

5. The charm of this musical comedy lies in its slam-bang pacing, its sprightly music, and its generally (**onerous, ebullient**) good cheer.

6. What appeared to be an informal study group was in reality a highly organized (**detritus, cabal**) determined to overthrow the establishment.

7. Though the presidency confers great powers on the person who holds the office, it also saddles that person with (**onerous, eclectic**) responsibilities.

8. It is one thing to (**burnish, deprecate**) human follies and pretensions; it is quite another to correct them.

9. The (**moribund, burnished**) helmets and breastplates of the warriors gleamed and twinkled in the morning sunlight.

10. No one, however powerful or dominant, can (**abrogate, sequester**) the basic moral laws on which civilization rests.

11. Writing that is so full of soggy clichés, gummy sentence structure, and excessive wordiness can best be described as (**inexorable, flaccid**).

12. (**Eclectic, Ambient**) schools of art are typical of a period when there is little original inspiration or bold experimentation.

13. Since archaeologists spend a lot of time rummaging through the (**detritus, asperity**) of vanished civilizations, they bear a striking resemblance to junk collectors and ragpickers.

14. Though skeptics insist that patriotism is (**onerous, moribund**) in America, I believe that it is alive and well in the hearts of the people.

15. The investigating committee spent long hours trying to (**burnish, winnow**) fact from fiction in the witnesses' testimony.

16. As we sat in the locker room after our heartbreaking loss, the (**ambient, impecunious**) gloom was so thick you could almost cut it.

17. Any political party that is (**rife, ebullient**) with petty jealousies and backbiting can never hope to present a united front in an election.

18. (**Asperity, Necromancy**) and other forms of witchcraft were punishable by death during the Middle Ages.

19. As one veteran aptly observed, a soldier had to be hardy to cope with the (**asperities, cabals**) of life in the trenches during World War I.

20. Anyone who has the slightest acquaintance with the (**rudiments, cabals**) of economic theory understands that we cannot solve our financial problems simply by borrowing more and more money.

21. Despite our prodding, Aunt Eileen would not disclose the secret ingredient that makes her marinara sauce so (**delectable, ebullient**).

22. The film critic complained that some of the (**sequestered, inexorable**) tension in the original film has been lost in this year's milder remake.

23. The unconventional artist liked to incorporate glass shards, plastic strips, pieces of string, and assorted (**detritus, rudiments**) into his sculptures.

24. "Did you use a cotton or a velvet cloth to (**burnish, abrogate**) the antique mirror?" Bryan inquired.

25. The (**cabal, asperity**) of the stones in the patio hurt the soles of my feet.

Synonyms

*Choose the word from this unit that is the same or most nearly the same in meaning as the **boldface** word or expression in the phrase. Write that word on the line. Use a dictionary if necessary.*

1. cleaned up the **debris** from the parade   _____

2. **secluded** on a remote country estate   _____

3. a ruthless **clique** of gangsters   _____

4. the **inescapable** consequences of her actions   _____

5. a garden **filled** with weeds   _____

6. a **varied collection** of opinions   _____

7. the **exuberant** cheerleading squad   _____

8. sheltered the **penniless** immigrants   _____

9. rebelled against the **oppressive** taxation   _____

10. noticed another **fading** tradition   _____

Antonyms

*Choose the word from this unit that is most nearly opposite in meaning to the **boldface** word or expression in the phrase. Write that word on the line. Use a dictionary if necessary.*

1. will **reaffirm** his oath to the king _____

2. noticed her **firm** handshake _____

3. a snack **low in** nutritional value _____

4. the **flourishing** downtown area _____

5. **countenanced** our peaceful protest _____

Completing the Sentence

From the words in this unit, choose the one that best completes each of the following sentences. Write the word in the space provided.

1. I thought the job of revising the manuscript would be a relatively simple matter, but it proved to be a(n) __onerous__ task.

2. Some superstitious Roman emperors consulted __necromancers__ and other dabblers in black magic to find out what the future held.

3. The plot of the novel centers on a(n) __impecunious__ adventurer who attempts to remedy his financial embarrassment by marrying into money.

4. The copper pots had been so highly __burnished__ that I could see my face in them.

5. Though monarchies still exist in some parts of the world, they are more or less a(n) __moribund__ form of government.

6. One of Darwin's theories suggests that nature ensures the survival of a species by slowly __winnowing__ out the less fit members.

7. There is nothing more __delectable__ on a hot day than to stretch out in a hammock with a good book and pitcher of icy lemonade!

8. I could tell that my boss was really "riled" by the __asperity__ of his tone of voice when he summoned me.

9. The conversation at dinner tables all over town was __rife__ with speculation as to the outcome of the big game.

10. All the facts and figures point to one __inexorable__ conclusion: we are hopelessly outnumbered.

11. We will never allow anyone to curtail or _____ the basic rights and liberties guaranteed to us in the Constitution.

12. She is a very private person who _____ any attempt to honor publicly her great services to humanity.

13. Even before they said a word, I could tell from their _____ expressions that our team had won.

14. Late that night, we began the heartbreaking task of sifting through the _____ of our ravaged home.

15. Unless you have mastered the _____ of French grammar, you will find it difficult to speak the language fluently.

16. As air slowly seeped out through the tiny puncture, the inner tube became more and more _____.

17. It was then that he began to organize the _____ that would later depose the king.

18. In order to prevent outside influences from coming into play, a jury is normally _____ until it reaches a decision.

19. It is often difficult to hold a conversation while walking on a busy city street because of the high level of _____ traffic noise.

20. In a sense, the man is a(n) _____ philosopher because his ideas have been influenced by many different schools of thought.

Writing: Words in Action

1. Look back at "Apollo 11 Poised for Take-Off" (pages 136–137). If you were offered the opportunity, would you like to be a passenger on a space flight to the moon? Why or why not? In a short expository essay, explain your opinion, using at least two details from the passage and three unit words.

2. In recent years, the United States has reduced funding for its manned space exploration programs. Some people argue that the money spent on space exploration could be better used elsewhere. However, others claim that the potential benefits of space exploration justify its costs. In your opinion, how important is continued manned space exploration? Explain your position on this question in a short essay. Use specific examples from your reading (refer to pages 136–137), studies, and personal observations to support your point. Write at least three paragraphs, and use at least three words from this unit.

Vocabulary in Context

Literary Text

The following excerpts are from Anthony Trollope's novels The Eustace Diamonds *and* Barchester Towers. *Some of the words you have studied in this unit appear in* **boldface** *type. Complete each statement below the excerpt by circling the letter of the correct answer.*

1. Frank began pretty well, getting some little work in London, and perhaps nearly enough to pay the cost of his circuit out of the county in which the cathedral was situated. But he began life after that **impecunious** fashion for which the Greystocks had been noted. (*The Eustace Diamonds*)

   An **impecunious** life is NOT
   a. random
   b. prosperous
   c. lively
   d. bland

2. Having pronounced this terrible sentence, Mrs. Carbunkle stalked out of the room. "That they can **sequester** your property for your creditors, I know," she said, returning for a moment and putting her head within the door. (*The Eustace Diamonds*)

   To **sequester** is to
   a. auction off
   b. abandon
   c. take possession of
   d. display

3. Now, Dr. Proudie certainly liked the lady, but, seeing that he was a bishop, it was not probable that he was going to instruct a little girl in the first **rudiments** of her catechism; so he said he'd send a teacher. (*Barchester Towers*)

   Rudiments are
   a. facts
   b. performances
   c. strict rituals
   d. the earliest stages

Anthony Trollope was one of the most prolific Victorian novelists, writing 47 novels before his death in 1882. Above, an illustration from one of his novels

4. Even the compliment did not soften the **asperity** of the maimed beauty. "Every woman is charming according to Lotte," she said; "I never knew an eye with so little true appreciation." (*Barchester Towers*)

   Asperity is
   a. admiration
   b. brilliance
   c. severity
   d. judgment

5. Mr. Slope's only preferment has hitherto been that of reader and preacher in a London district church; and on the consecration of his friend the new bishop, he readily gave this up to undertake the **onerous** but congenial duties of domestic chaplain to his lordship. (*Barchester Towers*)

   Duties that are **onerous** are
   a. burdensome
   b. virtuous
   c. traditional
   d. abundant

Snap the code, or go to **vocabularyworkshop.com**

*Read the following selection, taking note of the **boldface** words and their contexts. These words are among those you will be studying in Unit 12. As you complete the exercises in this unit, it may help to refer to the way the words are used below.*

Pyramids: Monuments to Gods and Men

<Compare and Contrast Essay>

Imposing, mysterious pyramids, found in areas from Asia to the Middle East to South America, have fascinated people for millennia. Some pyramids are lauded for their **aesthetic** qualities; some, though not as beautiful, are equally intriguing. Who built these architectural wonders? Why were they built, and what is their significance? And how were they built, given the technological limitations?

The world's largest pyramids are in Egypt, in the Valley of the Kings, near Cairo, and in Teotihuacan, in proximity to Mexico City, where these massive constructions seem **omnipresent** and command the attention of all onlookers. The two pyramids were built for different reasons—as tombs for Egypt's pharaohs and as places of worship and ritual for the Teotihuacans, but **impeccable** planning went into the erecting of each.

The Great Pyramid of Giza (also known as the Great Pyramid of Khufu, or Cheops) was one of the Seven Wonders of the Ancient World. It was constructed circa 2560 B.C. and is made up of 2.3 million limestone blocks. Estimates vary, but it took perhaps 30,000 men 20 years to complete the first Great Pyramid and its remarkable complex of secret chambers and hidden passages. It was created as a tomb for Pharoah Khufu, who **espoused** a belief in the afterlife and wanted a resting place for himself, his wives, and his treasures within a structure that would thwart and **discomfit** his enemies. Nearby, as part of the Giza Necropolis, are another two pyramids and the Great

Ancient artifacts have been uncovered from the pyramids and other monuments in Giza, Egypt.

Sphinx. All have withstood the natural elements: As an old proverb says, the pyramids mock time.

Unlike Egyptian pyramids, Mesoamerican pyramids are typically step pyramids with a temple at the peak. The three magnificent pyramids of Teotihuacan—the Pyramid of the Moon, the Pyramid of the Sun and the Feathered Serpent Pyramid—are part of a massive archaeological site in the Basin of Mexico. The main street, the "Avenue of the Dead," is lined with smaller temples and residences, and excavations throughout the site have turned up fertility **fetishes** and other talismans. The largest structure, the Pyramid of the Sun, was completed by A.D. 100 and is about half as tall as the Great Pyramid of Giza. The pyramid's core was mainly volcanic ash and gravel, while a thick layer of stone and mortar made up its walls. Incredibly, the builders were able to erect these marvels without the aid of the wheel or metal tools.

The early history of Teotihuacan is enigmatic because no one is completely sure which ancient, **gregarious** society built North America's first great city. The inhabitants used the pyramids in their religious rites and sacrifices. Ignoring the **plaintive** wails of their **hapless** victims, they **importuned** the gods for favors. The city's **nadir** came about A.D. 600, when the Teotihuacans abandoned their home, but a later Indian civilization, the Aztecs, adopted the city and kept it from becoming **defunct**. They dubbed the place the "City of the Gods," or "Place Where Men Become Gods."

Over time, explorers and treasure hunters have done lasting and **irreparable** damage to the world's pyramids, including those in Egypt and Teotihuacan. In many cases, authorities have made inferior, **perfunctory** repairs or allowed the damaged pyramids to **languish** and fall into disrepair, but now both sites are protected as national treasures by their governments. Thousands of tourists visit the pyramids in the Valley of the Kings and Teotihuacan every year.

iWords

Snap the code, or go to
vocabularyworkshop.com

Ceramics such as this seated figure were found at Teotihuacan in Mexico.

Definitions

Note the spelling, pronunciation, part(s) of speech, and definition(s) of each of the following words. Then write the word in the blank spaces in the illustrative sentence(s) following. Finally, study the lists of synonyms and antonyms.

1. aesthetic
(es thet′ ik)

(*adj.*) pertaining to beauty; sensitive or responsive to beauty

Since the structure had no practical purpose, keeping it in place could only be justified on _____ grounds.

SYNONYM: artistic

2. defunct
(di fəŋkt′)

(*adj.*) no longer in existence or functioning, dead

I could find no forwarding address or phone number for the _____ organization.

SYNONYMS: extinct, nonexistent
ANTONYM: alive

3. discomfit
(dis kəm′ fit)

(*v.*) to frustrate, thwart, or defeat; to confuse, perplex, or embarrass

The general tried to _____ his enemies by repeatedly beginning an advance and then pulling back.

SYNONYMS: nonplus, foil

4. espouse
(es paüz′)

(*v.*) to take up and support; to become attached to, adopt; to marry

To appeal to the large number of dissatisfied voters, the candidate _____ a strong program of reform.

SYNONYMS: embrace, wed
ANTONYMS: repudiate, disavow, renounce

5. fetish
(fet′ ish)

(*n.*) an object believed to have magical powers; an object of unreasoning devotion or reverence

The rabbit's foot, once a very popular _____, seems to have lost its hold on the public imagination.

SYNONYMS: charm, obsession

6. gregarious
(grə gār′ ē əs)

(*adj.*) living together in a herd or group; sociable, seeking the company of others

I would expect the recreation director of a cruise ship to be a _____ person.

SYNONYMS: outgoing, extroverted
ANTONYMS: aloof, introverted, reclusive

7. hapless
(hap′ lis)

(*adj.*) marked by a persistent absence of good luck

Once again, my younger brother has become the
_____ victim of a silly practical joke.

SYNONYMS: unlucky, ill-starred, unfortunate
ANTONYMS: lucky, charmed, fortunate

8. impeccable
(im pek′ ə bəl)

(*adj.*) faultless, beyond criticism or blame

We always consulted my grandmother about what to wear
because she had _____ taste in clothing.

SYNONYMS: flawless, spotless, immaculate
ANTONYMS: grimy, soiled, spotted

9. importune
(im pôr tyün′)

(*v.*) to trouble with demands; to beg for insistently

My bankrupt uncle _____ my father
for a loan.

SYNONYMS: implore, dun, tax

10. interpolate
(in tər′ pə lāt)

(*v.*) to insert between other parts or things; to present as an
addition or correction

At the director's request, the screenwriter
_____ some new lines into the script.

SYNONYMS: interpose, introduce

11. irreparable
(i rep′ ər ə bəl)

(*adj.*) incapable of being repaired or rectified

The husband believed that the surgeon did
_____ harm to his wife and sued
the doctor and the hospital.

SYNONYM: irremediable
ANTONYMS: remediable, fixable, reversible

12. laconic
(lə kän′ ik)

(*adj.*) concise, using few words

The senator issued a _____ statement
declaring her innocence after the accusations of fraud were
made public.

SYNONYMS: succinct, pithy, compact
ANTONYMS: garrulous, prolix, loquacious

13. languish
(laŋ′ gwish)

(*v.*) to become weak, feeble, or dull; to droop; to be depressed or
dispirited; to suffer neglect

Without the constitutional guarantee of a speedy trial, the
accused could _____ in jail for years.

SYNONYMS: flag, fade, pine

14. mendacious
(men dā 'shəs)

(*adj.*) given to lying or deception; untrue

The deputy gave a _____ account of his employer's actions on the day of the alleged crime.

SYNONYMS: untruthful, false
ANTONYM: veracious

15. nadir
(nā' dər)

(*n.*) the lowest point

At the _____ of his popularity, the prime minister decided to resign his office and call for new elections.

SYNONYMS: rock bottom
ANTONYMS: pinnacle, zenith

16. omnipresent
(äm ni pre' zənt)

(*adj.*) present in all places at all times

They believed in an _____ deity that existed in all things.

SYNONYMS: ubiquitous, ever-present

17. perfunctory
(per fəŋk' tə rē)

(*adj.*) done in a superficial or halfhearted manner; without interest or enthusiasm

The police made a _____ search for the missing handbag, but they really did not expect to find it.

SYNONYMS: slapdash, shallow
ANTONYMS: thorough, assiduous, diligent, meticulous

18. plaintive
(plān' tiv)

(*adj.*) expressive of sorrow or woe, melancholy

The recently widowed man spoke of his loneliness in a _____ tone of voice.

SYNONYMS: sad, lugubrious
ANTONYMS: cheerful, blithe, joyous, merry

19. requite
(ri kwīt')

(*v.*) to make suitable repayment, as for a kindness, service, or favor; to make retaliation, as for an injury or wrong; to reciprocate

We made sure to _____ the neighbors for looking after our house while we were away.

SYNONYMS: reimburse, avenge

20. tantamount
(tan' tə maůnt)

(*adj.*) equivalent, having the same meaning, value, or effect

The armed invasion of their territory was _____ to a declaration of war.

SYNONYM: indistinguishable from

Choosing the Right Word

*Select the **boldface** word that better completes each sentence. You might refer to the selection on pages 146–147 to see how most of these words are used in context.*

1. One of the best-known figures of American folklore is the lean, tough, (**laconic, hapless**) cowboy.

2. I hope to (**espouse, requite**) my parents for all the care they have shown me.

3. Although fate has decreed that he make his living as a stockbroker, his main interests and talents are definitely (**irreparable, aesthetic**).

4. Though I left the house feeling "as fit as a fiddle," my spirits began to (**requite, languish**) after only five minutes in that withering heat.

The popularity of cowboy music grew after the recording of the first cowboy song in 1925.

5. Her sense of tact is so (**hapless, impeccable**) and unerring that she can handle the most trying situation as if it were mere child's play.

6. The sternness of my boss's expression so (**discomfited, languished**) me that at first I had difficulty responding to the question.

7. Many scholars believe that Beaumont or Fletcher (**interpolated, requited**) a scene or two into the present text of Shakespeare's *Macbeth*.

8. One of the comforting things about reaching the (**fetish, nadir**) of one's career is that the only place to go from there is up.

9. Perhaps we should be overjoyed that the great man condescended to give us a(n) (**aesthetic, perfunctory**) nod as we passed by.

10. Though few of us today stand on ceremony to quite the extent that our ancestors did, common courtesy is by no means (**plaintive, defunct**).

11. Prehistoric peoples banded together into tribes, not only for protection, but also to satisfy their (**gregarious, mendacious**) instincts.

12. She sang a (**laconic, plaintive**) little ditty about a man who yearns wistfully for the girl he left behind many years before.

13. A diplomat must always proceed on the assumption that no rupture between nations, no matter how serious, is (**irreparable, perfunctory**).

14. The (**omnipresent, gregarious**) threat of a nuclear holocaust that characterized the Cold War era changed many people's attitudes toward war in profound ways.

15. The legal adage "Silence implies consent" means that not objecting to an action that concerns you is (**perfunctory, tantamount**) to approving it.

16. In our desire to improve the quality of life in America, we should not be too quick to (**importune, espouse**) an idea simply because it is new.

17. When the scandal broke, the man found himself the (**hapless, impeccable**) victim of other people's misdeeds.

18. It is one thing to be concerned about discipline; it is quite another to make a (**perfunctory, fetish**) of it.

19. I don't know which is more painful—to have to ask someone for a favor or to have some unfortunate (**importune, discomfit**) one for help.

20. Fortunately, our lawyer was able to produce documents that disproved the (**mendacious, omnipresent**) assertions of our former partner.

21. Faced with a tight deadline, the exhausted editor gave the young reporter's article a hurried and (**perfunctory, gregarious**) edit.

22. In the *Poetics* and the *Metaphysics*, Greek philosopher Aristotle discusses the purpose of art and identifies important (**omnipresent, aesthetic**) principles.

23. After the death of his wife of seven decades, a grieving Mr. Johnson (**languished, espoused**) in their quiet apartment.

24. "Despite taking an oath to tell the truth, Laurie offered clearly (**tantamount, mendacious**) testimony," complained the frustrated defense attorney.

25. The whiny toddler (**importuned, requited**) his mother for a snack.

Synonyms

*Choose the word from this unit that is the same or most nearly the same in meaning as the **boldface** word or expression in the phrase. Write that word on the line. Use a dictionary if necessary.*

1. recompensed them for their hospitality   _____

2. tried to **interject** a different opinion   _____

3. entreated the governor for a pardon   _____

4. cautioned me against the **dishonest** salesperson   _____

5. disconcerted the conservative audience   _____

6. kept repeating that **doleful** melody   _____

7. wilt under the hot sun   _____

8. listened to a **terse** summary   _____

9. no more than a **cursory** note of apology   _____

10. equal to betraying a friend   _____

Antonyms

*Choose the word from this unit that is most nearly opposite in meaning to the **boldface** word or expression in the phrase. Write that word on the line. Use a dictionary if necessary.*

1. **spurn** her desire for friendship   _____

2. gave a **verbose** tribute to his partner   _____

3. **unlike** a fair deal   _____

4. prone to **delete** unimportant text   _____

5. a **truthful** account of the events   _____

Completing the Sentence

From the words in this unit, choose the one that best completes each of the following sentences. Write the word in the space provided.

1. I was greatly relieved to learn that the accident I had with my car last week didn't do any _____ damage to the motor.

2. Every general seems to have one defeat that marks the _____ of his military fortunes—for example, Lee at Gettysburg or Grant at Cold Harbor.

3. One wall of the museum was filled with charms and _____ designed to ward off everything from a hangnail to the evil eye.

4. They claim to have made a thorough search of the premises, but I suspect that their efforts were no more than _____.

5. Last night, Central High's Shooting Stars captured the basketball championship by _____ the South High Slammers, 61 to 44.

6. When you get more experience on the job, you will learn that a "request" from your employer is _____ to an order.

7. No matter where candidates for high political office go these days, the _____ eye of the TV camera seems focused on them.

8. "Don't you think it's a little foolish to pursue the young lady when your warm feelings for her are clearly not _____?" I asked.

9. Since extroverts are _____ by nature, they usually prefer not to live alone.

10. Responding to the melancholy note in the song of the nightingale, Keats wrote of its "_____ anthem."

11. To say that he is _____ does not even begin to convey just how alienated he is from any regard for the truth.

12. Never once has the least whiff of a scandal or impropriety tainted the man's _____ reputation as an upstanding member of this agency.

13. I thought our state legislators would consider the proposal at the earliest opportunity, but they let it _____ in committee for months.

14. From a(n) _____ point of view, the painting didn't appeal to me, but I kept it because it was a memento of my childhood.

15. Suddenly I was surrounded by a mob of street urchins loudly _____ me for a handout.

16. It's easy enough to back a popular program, but it takes real courage to _____ a cause that most people oppose.

17. I felt a little foolish when the librarian told me that I was asking for the current issue of a magazine that had long been _____.

18. The _____ creature had somehow gotten its foot caught in the grate and could not extricate it without help.

19. As his irrepressible flow of reminiscences continued without a letup, I tried in vain to _____ a few observations of my own.

20. When asked what terms he would offer the Confederate army, General Grant made the _____ reply, "Unconditional surrender!"

Writing: Words in Action

1. Look back at "Pyramids: Monuments to Gods and Men" (pages 146–147). Suppose that you are helping to raise funds to repair the pyramids in Egypt or Teotihuacan. You want to persuade contributors to make a donation by convincing them that the pyramids have historical and cultural significance, not only to Egypt or Mexico but also to the world. Write a persuasive business letter, using at least two details from the passage and three unit words.

2. *"Those who cannot remember the past are condemned to repeat it."*
   —George Santayana

   Do you agree with poet and philosopher George Santayana's statement about remembering the past? How important is it for high school students to study world history, to learn, for example, about the ancient civilizations of Egypt and Teotihuacan? In a brief expository essay, explain your opinion with specific examples from your studies, observations and experiences, or current events. Write at least three paragraphs, and use three or more words from this unit.

Vocabulary in Context

Literary Text

The following excerpts are from James Fenimore Cooper's novels The Last of the Mohicans *and* The Pioneers. *Some of the words you have studied in this unit appear in* **boldface** *type. Complete each statement below the excerpt by circling the letter of the correct answer.*

1. "Why die at all!" said Cora, advancing from the place where natural horror had, until this moment, held her riveted to the rock; "the path is open on every side; fly, then, to the woods, and call on God for succor. Go, brave men, we owe you too much already; let us no longer involve you in our **hapless** fortunes!" (*The Last of the Mohicans*)

    Something that is **hapless** is NOT

    a. relevant   **c.** predictable
    b. impressive   **d.** lucky

2. Heyward gathered from the manners of the different speakers, that the father and son **espoused** one side of a disputed question, while the white man maintained the other. (*The Last of the Mohicans*)

    If something is **espoused**, it is

    a. investigated   **c.** supported
    b. rejected   **d.** debated

3. "His time has come," said the **laconic** scout, thrusting the long barrel of his rifle through the leaves, and taking his deliberate and fatal aim. But, instead of pulling the trigger he lowered the muzzle again, and indulged himself in a fit of his peculiar mirth. (*The Last of the Mohicans*)

    Someone who is **laconic**

    a. uses few words   **c.** shows no fear
    b. acts impulsively   **d.** appears fatigued

    Wood engraving from an 1872 edition of *The Last of the Mohicans*

4. "Nay, Natty," rejoined the traveller, with undisturbed good-humor, "it is for the honor that I contend. A few dollars will pay for the venison, but what will **requite** me for the lost honor of a buck's tail in my cap?" (*The Pioneers*)

    To **requite** is to

    a. annoy slightly   **c.** produce shame
    b. repay suitably   **d.** offer revenge

5. Once, just as her eyes had opened, apparently in the last stage of drowsiness, the roaring winds brought with them a long and **plaintive** howl, that seemed too wild for a dog, and yet resembled the cries of that faithful animal, when night awakens his vigilance, and gives sweetness and solemnity to its charms. (*The Pioneers*)

    Something that is **plaintive** is

    a. melancholy   **c.** fierce
    b. shrill   **d.** jubilant

Snap the code, or go to
vocabularyworkshop.com

Vocabulary for Comprehension

*Read the following selection in which some of the words you have studied in Units 10–12 appear in **boldface** type. Then answer the questions on page 157.*

This passage focuses on the brief but remarkable era of silent films.

(Line)

It may be tempting for modern viewers to **deprecate** silent films. After all, they are technically primitive compared with today's

(5) movies. Much of the acting is exaggerated and overwrought, and the plots are often melodramatic or sentimental. Also, there is no dialogue except for some **laconic**

(10) titles that appear on the screen from time to time. Yet in their day, audiences flocked to see these movies, marveling at the **luminous** images on the flickering screen. To

(15) these enthusiastic new moviegoers, there was nothing as exciting as moving pictures!

Two men, Louis Lumiere and Thomas Alva Edison, one French

(20) and one American, are usually credited with the invention of the motion picture camera. In 1895 Louis Lumiere invented what he called the *cinematographe*. This compact,

(25) versatile instrument was **tantamount** to a camera, film-processing unit, and projector all in one. Because

Edison's camera was bulkier and less portable than Lumiere's, the

(30) Europeans took an early lead in the development of motion pictures. The Americans soon caught up, however, and Hollywood eventually became the capital of a vastly profitable

(35) international film industry that began in the 1910s with the production of silent movies.

Many contemporary viewers have overlooked the masterpieces of the

(40) silent era because they find the adjustments they must make to watch these films **onerous**. Without knowing it, however, they are depriving themselves of some

(45) unparalleled pleasures. These include the brilliant physical comedy of Buster Keaton, the visual expressiveness of Charlie Chaplin, and the landmark editing, camera

(50) work, and set designs of the great pioneer filmmakers D.W. Griffith, Sergei Eisenstein, F.R. Murnau, and Fritz Lang.

1. In the first paragraph (lines 1–17), the writer's main focus is on
   a. discussing camera types
   b. introducing some of the writer's favorite silent films
   c. contrasting the drawbacks of silent films with the excitement they inspired in audiences of the day
   d. describing landmark camera work
   e. comparing Keaton and Chaplin

2. The meaning of **deprecate** (line 2) is
   a. belittle
   b. ignore
   c. overpraise
   d. underestimate
   e. misunderstand

3. In paragraph 1, the author mentions all of the following as drawbacks of silent films EXCEPT
   a. melodramatic plots
   b. overwrought acting
   c. laconic captions
   d. unattractive set designs
   e. primitive technical achievements

4. **Laconic** (line 9) most nearly means
   a. brilliant
   b. obscure
   c. succinct
   d. humorous
   e. redundant

5. **Luminous** (line 13) is best defined as
   a. timeless
   b. blurred
   c. bright
   d. lifelike
   e. shocking

6. From the details given in paragraph 2 (lines 18–37), one may reasonably infer that the Americans caught up with the Europeans because
   a. the leading actors were American
   b. refinements made film equipment less bulky and more portable
   c. the Americans made more films
   d. Hollywood was appealing
   e. Lumiere's equipment often broke

7. **Tantamount** (line 25) most nearly means
   a. similar
   b. supplementary
   c. opposed
   d. compared
   e. equivalent

8. In paragraph 2, it may be inferred that the author believes that the *cinematographe* was
   a. expensive
   b. worthless
   c. useful
   d. disappointing
   e. beautiful

9. According to the passage, the international film industry began in
   a. the 1930s
   b. the 1920s
   c. the 1910s
   d. the 1890s
   e. the 1880s

10. In paragraph 3 (lines 38–53), the writer most likely includes so many examples in order to
    a. explain the cost of silent movies
    b. trace the ways in which silent film stars influenced one another
    c. persuade the reader of the claims made for silent films in the passage
    d. display a high level of expertise
    e. prove that directors were more skilled than actors

11. **Onerous** (line 42) most nearly means
    a. annoying
    b. costly
    c. silly
    d. burdensome
    e. easy

12. The writer's attitude toward silent films might best be described as
    a. enthusiastic
    b. skeptical
    c. respectful
    d. neutral
    e. dismissive

Two-Word Completions

Select the pair of words that best complete the meaning of each of the following passages.

1. In *Of Human Bondage,* W. Somerset Maugham's main character Philip Carey is _____ by external adversity as well as his own self-consciousness because he was so _____ as to have been born with a club foot.
   a. rebuffed . . . sporadic
   b. requited . . . benign
   c. decimated . . . laconic
   d. discomfited . . . hapless

2. Though the man appeared to be the most _____ pauper on the face of the earth, he had actually _____ large sums of money in various hiding places in the hovel he called home.
   a. flaccid . . . burnished
   b. impecunious . . . sequestered
   c. ambient . . . interpolated
   d. benign . . . decimated

3. As soon as I heard its _____ cries for help, I knew that the _____ animal had once again got its paw caught in the grillwork on the front porch.
   a. obsequious . . . moribund
   b. laconic . . . impeccable
   c. onerous . . . defunct
   d. plaintive . . . hapless

4. Although many of the pioneers found it difficult at first to cope with the _____ of frontier life, they were a hardy race who quickly became _____ such rough-and-tumble living.
   a. rudiments . . . importuned by
   b. asperities . . . inured to
   c. detritus . . . decimated by
   d. shambles . . . discomfited by

5. Though Seneca embraced the tenets of Stoicism in their entirety, Cicero _____ not just one school of Greek philosophy but, like a true _____, chose what he thought best from each.
   a. discomfited . . . penitent
   b. abrogated . . . aesthetic
   c. espoused . . . eclectic
   d. deprecated . . . foible

6. The "truth-in-advertising" laws that many states have passed were designed to stop crooks and _____ from making _____ claims about the products they offer to the unsuspecting public.
   a. charlatans . . . mendacious
   b. necromancers . . . sporadic
   c. fetishes . . . laconic
   d. cabals . . . eclectic

7. The dietician looked _____ at the sugary cereal and suggested that we _____ it and try whole-wheat toast and fruit instead.
   a. ambient . . . attenuate
   b. askance . . . forgo
   c. tantamount . . . cavil
   d. obtuse . . . winnow

Proverbs

In the passage about the mystery of the Franklin Expedition (see page 127), the author notes that "a string of facts does not add up to the truth." This saying is a proverb. The author means that the pieces of evidence that were found on Franklin's vessels (the facts) do not provide a full explanation of what happened to Franklin and his crew (the truth).

A **proverb** is a traditional and brief saying that expresses advice or a widely recognized truth about life in a memorable way. Proverbs may owe their appeal to a play on words (*Don't bite off more than you can chew*), an unusual metaphor (*A clear conscience is a soft pillow*), effective parallel structure (*Justice delayed is justice denied*), or even rhyme (*A friend in need is a friend indeed*).

Choosing the Right Proverb

Read each sentence. Use context clues to figure out the meaning of each proverb in **boldface** *print. Then write the letter of the definition for the proverb in the sentence.*

1. When my friend broke up with her boyfriend, I reminded her that **there are other fish in the sea**. _____

2. Be sure that you have completed each line of the application. Remember, **for want of a nail, the kingdom was lost**. _____

3. "Don't get discouraged because you didn't make the team," the coach said to the athlete. "**When one door closes, another one opens**." _____

4. "**Don't bite the hand that feeds you**," Grandpa said when I complained about Dad's work hours. _____

5. There is no use asking Troy to pay rent since he's been living here free. After all, **give a man an inch and he'll take a mile**. _____

6. It means little that we lost the game by only one touchdown because **a miss is as good as a mile**. _____

7. Mr. Chang advised, "You should pay your credit card bills now, since **out of debt, out of danger**." _____

8. "I have no desire for a promotion," Sally said. "**The highest branch is not the safest roost**." _____

9. **Pride goes before a fall**, which may be why the singer who predicted she would win the talent competition now has laryngitis. _____

10. If we want the senator to vote against the bill, we need to publicize our complaints because **the squeaky wheel gets the grease**. _____

a. Failure is often followed by a new opportunity.

b. Overconfidence can lead to trouble.

c. People are inclined to take advantage of others' generosity.

d. Those who make the most fuss get what they want.

e. Nobody who owes money is secure.

f. Do not neglect small details.

g. Be kind to those on whom you depend.

h. Other people and other opportunities are available.

i. Those with the most power are often the most uneasy.

j. If you fail, the margin of failure doesn't matter.

Writing with Proverbs

Find the meaning of each proverb. (Use an online or print dictionary if necessary.) Then write a sentence for each proverb.

1. Life is no bed of roses.

_____

2. Strike while the iron is hot.

_____

3. Dig the well before you are thirsty.

_____

4. As you sow, so shall you reap.

_____

5. Always put your best foot forward.

_____

6. A bad workman quarrels with his tools.

_____

_____

7. You can lead a horse to water, but you can't make him drink.

_____

_____

8. Fools rush in where angels fear to tread.

_____

_____

9. Might makes right.

_____

10. One good turn deserves another.

_____

11. What's good for the goose is good for the gander.

_____

12. The eye is bigger than the belly.

_____

Denotation and Connotation

To speak or write with precision, you need to know both the denotation and the connotation of the words you use. The **denotation** is the literal dictionary meaning of a word. A word's **connotation** is the emotional implications and associations that a word can have. Connotations may be *positive*, *negative*, or *neutral*.

Consider these synonyms for the word *obsequious*:

> *amenable   complaisant   servile   sycophantic*

Amenable and *complaisant* refer to positive behaviors marked by respect and a disposition to please. *Servile* and *sycophantic* refer to negative behaviors, characterized by fawning and excessive submissiveness.

> **Think:** A cooperative worker is amenable and complaisant when working with others, but a self-serving employee is servile or sycophantic.

Look at these examples of words that are similar in denotation but have different connotations.

NEUTRAL	POSITIVE	NEGATIVE
emotional	sentimental	plaintive
attribute	virtue	foible
inactive	relaxed	flaccid

Writers and speakers need to analyze nuances in the meaning of words with similar denotations. They should choose the word that best conveys the exact meaning and tone they intend. Selecting a word with positive connotations in a situation that calls for a negative or neutral term (or vice versa) can distract or confuse the audience.

Shades of Meaning

Write a plus sign (+) in the box if the word has a positive connotation.
Write a minus sign (–) if the word has a negative connotation. Put a zero (0)
if the word is neutral.

1. attenuate ☐   **2.** delectable ☐   **3.** ambient ☐   **4.** rife ☐

5. discomfit ☐   **6.** interpolate ☐   **7.** moribund ☐   **8.** impecunious ☐

9. gregarious ☐   **10.** abrogate ☐   **11.** irreparable ☐   **12.** languish ☐

13. sequester ☐   **14.** impeccable ☐   **15.** onerous ☐   **16.** reconnoiter ☐

Expressing the Connotation

Read each sentence. Select the word in parentheses that expresses the connotation (positive, negative, or neutral) given at the beginning of the sentence.

neutral   **1.** The timid student tried to make sense of the (**cavil, observation**) the teacher wrote in the margins of the essay.

positive   **2.** The desert scene was beautiful, with the sand and palm trees bathed in (**luminous, glaring**) moonlight.

negative   **3.** After watching Roger bumble about in the kitchen, I realized he was not a skilled chef, but rather a(n) (**amateur, charlatan**).

neutral   **4.** Ruth's (**response, rebuff**) to the stranger's offer to take her photograph in front of the White House surprised our entire family.

negative   **5.** The high winds and torrential rains (**decimated, transformed**) the newly planted rose gardens.

neutral   **6.** After a difficult loss, the team captain (**deprecated, delineated**) the effort shown by his teammates.

positive   **7.** The (**ebullient, agitated**) crowd jammed the streets outside the football stadium after the Scouts' surprising victory in overtime.

negative   **8.** The lifeguards looked (**skeptically, askance**) at the antics of the children who were chasing the birds along the beach.

Challenge: Using Connotation

Choose vocabulary words from Units 10–12 to replace the highlighted words in the sentences below. Then explain how the connotation of the replacement word changes the tone of the sentence.

tantamount	**fraught**	**mendacious**
perfunctory	**penitent**	**benign**

1. After taking a **swift** _____ glance at the appointment book, the receptionist advised the client to call back later.

_____

_____

2. The pediatrician reassured the parents that letting little Marie suck her thumb frequently would have a **harmless** _____ influence on the baby's development.

_____

3. Mrs. Garcia suspected that the mechanic's detailed explanation of the problem with her car's engine was **questionable** _____.

_____

_____

Classical Roots

rog—to ask, beg, call

The root *rog* appears in **abrogate** (page 138), meaning "to cancel, to abolish by authoritative action." Some other words based on the same root are listed below.

abrogation	**derogation**	**interrogative**	**supererogatory**
arrogance	**interrogation**	**prorogue**	**surrogate**

From the list of words above, choose the one that corresponds to each of the brief definitions below. Write the word in the blank space in the illustrative sentence below the definition. Use an online or print dictionary if necessary.

1. a substitute, deputy; a judge in charge of the probate of wills, administration of estates, and appointment of guardians

   While my parents were on vacation, my aunt served as a
   _____ guardian.

2. performed or observed beyond the degree required; demanded, or expected; unnecessary; superfluous

   "We could do with fewer _____ remarks," the teacher observed.

3. a cancellation; the act of repealing or annulling (*"calling off"*)

   Unfavorable evidence has emerged, forcing the _____ of the agreement between the two parties.

4. exaggerated self-importance, haughty pride

   The king was corrupted by power and, over time, exchanged his humility for
   _____.

5. an act or expression that detracts from reputation, value, power, etc. (*"to call down"*)

   The aid workers deeply resented any _____ of their motives.

6. asking a question; having the form or character of a question; a word or sentence that asks a question

   In Spanish class, we are learning how to phrase _____ sentences.

7. to discontinue a session of a legislative body; to defer, postpone

   The prime minister was determined to _____ the legislative assembly until all members were present.

8. an act of formal or systematic questioning

   The detective asked question after question during the _____ of the prime suspect.

*Read the following selection, taking note of the **boldface** words and their contexts. These words are among those you will be studying in Unit 13. As you complete the exercises in this unit, it may help to refer to the way the words are used below.*

More Than Just a Pretty Face

<Profile>

One of many Hollywood stars who **mesmerized** moviegoers of the 1940s was Hedy Lamarr. But it was not only Lamarr's striking looks and dramatic talent that **engendered** admiration in audiences. As fans learned about the actress's life story, many became more interested in Lamarr herself than in the characters she portrayed in her work onscreen.

Born in 1914 in Vienna, Austria, Hedwig Kiesler was the only child of Jewish parents who encouraged their daughter to study ballet and piano. Hedy began her acting career as a teenager, appearing in a number of German films. In 1933, she played a lovesick young wife in a Czech film called *Ecstasy*, a suggestive film derided by **captious** critics as an **affront** to moral decency. Despite the **opprobrium** levied against the film, *Ecstasy* undeniably raised the young actress's profile.

Not long after the film's release, Hedy married Fritz Mandl, an arms manufacturer some thirteen years her senior. They were an **incongruous** couple, and Mandl proved a jealous and tyrannical husband. He forbade his wife from pursuing her acting career, and ordered her to accompany him to business meetings. Though frustrated with the relationship, Hedy enjoyed discussions of Mandl's business affairs and became acquainted with weapons systems technology. Soon, dismayed to learn that her husband was a Nazi sympathizer, Hedy fled Austria, escaping both her husband and the Nazis.

An undated portrait of Hedy Lamarr

Various rumors about the **machinations** of her escape would later surface. According to one story, the actress used sleeping pills to drug her maid, who had instructions from Mr. Mandl to see that his wife did not leave the house. Then Hedy put on the maid's uniform and fled through the servants' entrance.

However she escaped, it wasn't long before Hedy arrived in Hollywood and adopted her stage name, Hedy Lamarr. Soon she was starring in motion pictures; she appeared in 18 films during her heyday in the 1940s. Her biggest box-office success was *Samson and Delilah*, the highest-grossing movie of 1949.

While fans at the time recognized Lamarr as an **ethereal** beauty, few were **cognizant** of the celebrity's off-screen pursuits as an inventor. In 1940, in collaboration with her Hollywood neighbor, composer George Antheil, Lamarr developed a "Secret Communication System" designed to make the radio signals used to control missiles harder to detect or jam. With World War II underway, the duo received a patent for the design in 1942. Though their device was never produced, the underlying concept of "frequency hopping" proposed by Lamarr was implemented in a similar form by the United States military in later years, and eventually became an essential feature of wireless communication systems.

In a less **abstruse** contribution to the war effort, Lamarr, with other leading Hollywood actresses, toured major cities to promote the sale of war bonds to help fund the war. Lamarr visited 16 cities in ten days, selling a **putative** $25 million in war bonds in all. Sales received a boost from the unsurprising **efficacy** of Lamarr's offer to kiss any man who purchased $25,000 worth of war bonds—an offer that reportedly raised $7 million in one night.

Lamarr's career declined from 1950, as she gradually fell out of favor with audiences and was no longer considered a bankable **cynosure** in Hollywood. Over time, rumors of less than **decorous** behavior pursued her, including accusations of shoplifting. Lamarr seldom assented to interviews, and after dismissing the rumors as **canards**, she maintained her characteristic silence. Some fans admired Lamarr for not **deigning** to behave in a **contrite** manner, but the rumors proved hard to shake.

Still waters run deep, and there is little doubt that behind the **facade** of silence, Lamarr remained the intelligent and complex person she had always been behind the gloss of Hollywood celebrity. The Electronic Frontier Foundation recognized her talents when it gave Lamarr the Pioneer Award in 1997 for her invention. Lamarr died in 2000.

Snap the code, or go to
vocabularyworkshop.com

Lamarr gives the V-for-Victory sign while selling war bonds in 1942.

Definitions

Note the spelling, pronunciation, part(s) of speech, and definition(s) of each of the following words. Then write the word in the blank spaces in the illustrative sentence(s) following. Finally, study the lists of synonyms and antonyms.

1. abstruse
(ab strüs′)

(*adj.*) extremely difficult to understand

The physicist tried to explain her _____ research in the field of quantum mechanics.

SYNONYMS: arcane, recondite, occult
ANTONYMS: simple, straightforward

2. affront
(ə frənt′)

(*n.*) an open or intentional insult; a slight; (*v.*) to insult to one's face; to face in defiance, confront

The student felt that being referred to by number rather than by name was an _____ to her dignity.

In the nineteenth century, Irish immigrants to the United States were _____ by signs reading: No Irish Need Apply.

SYNONYMS: (*n.*) offense; (*v.*) offend
ANTONYMS: (*n., v.*) compliment, praise

3. canard
(kə närd′)

(*n.*) a false rumor, fabricated story

The tabloid journalist was responsible for spreading the _____ about the candidate's mental health.

SYNONYM: hoax

4. captious
(kap′ shəs)

(*adj.*) excessively ready to find fault; given to petty criticism; intended to trap, confuse, or show up

She is an invariably _____ critic.

SYNONYMS: faultfinding, carping
ANTONYM: uncritical

5. cognizant
(käg′ ni zənt)

(*adj.*) aware, knowledgeable, informed; having jurisdiction

Police officers must make sure that crime suspects are made _____ of their rights before they are questioned.

SYNONYM: acquainted
ANTONYMS: unaware, unconscious, oblivious

6. contrite
(kən trīt′)

(*adj.*) regretful for some misdeed or sin; plagued by a sense of guilt; thoroughly penitent

The convicted felon had the look of someone who was truly _____ and ready to pay for his crimes.

SYNONYMS: remorseful, rueful
ANTONYMS: unapologetic, impenitent

7. cynosure
(sī′ nə shür)

(*n.*) the center of attraction, attention, or interest; something that serves to guide or direct

For over a century, the Statue of Liberty has been the _____ for millions of immigrants entering New York Harbor.

SYNONYM: focus

8. decorous
(dek′ ər əs)

(*adj.*) well behaved, dignified, socially proper

On formal occasions, participants are expected to behave in a _____ manner.

SYNONYMS: seemly, becoming, tasteful
ANTONYMS: unbecoming, improper, tasteless

9. deign
(dān)

(*v.*) to think it appropriate or suitable to one's dignity to do something; to condescend

The enlisted men were surprised that the four-star general _____ to speak to them in the camp.

SYNONYM: deem

10. desiccated
(des′ ə kā tid)

(*adj., part.*) thoroughly dried out; divested of spirit or vitality; arid and uninteresting

The cornfield was _____ by the scorching sun after the long, hot summer without rain.

SYNONYMS: dehydrated, shriveled
ANTONYMS: sodden, waterlogged, drenched

11. efficacy
(ef′ ə kə sē)

(*n.*) the power to produce a desired result

The pharmaceutical company has done extensive research to prove the _____ of the new drug.

SYNONYMS: effectiveness, potency, reliability
ANTONYM: impotence

12. engender
(in jen′ dər)

(*v.*) to bring into existence, give rise to, produce; to come into existence, assume form

The university has made an appealing video in order to _____ student interest in studying abroad.

SYNONYMS: generate, cause, form; ANTONYMS: stop, deter

13. ethereal
(i thēr′ ē əl)

(*adj.*) light, airy, delicate; highly refined; suggesting what is heavenly (rather than earthbound)

The Renaissance painter Fra Angelico captured the _____ beauty of angels in his frescoes.

SYNONYMS: heavenly, celestial, gossamer
ANTONYMS: infernal, hellish, thick, heavy

14. facade
(fə säd′)

(*n.*) the front or face of a building; a surface appearance (as opposed to what may lie behind)

After years of neglect, the sooty _____ of the structure is finally getting a much needed cleaning.

SYNONYMS: exterior, surface, mask
ANTONYM: interior

15. ghoulish
(gül′ ish)

(*adj.*) revolting in an unnatural or morbid way; suggestive of someone who robs graves or otherwise preys on the dead

The _____ practice of grave robbing is motivated by the desire to find and sell valuables.

SYNONYMS: barbarous, monstrous

16. incongruous
(in kän′ grü əs)

(*adj.*) not in keeping, unsuitable, incompatible

Abraham Lincoln, the backwoods lawyer, and Mary Todd, the socialite, seemed an _____ couple.

SYNONYM: discordant
ANTONYMS: compatible, harmonious, consistent

17. machination
(mak ə nā′ shən)

(*n.*) a crafty, scheming, or underhanded action designed to accomplish some (usually evil) end

Shakespeare's Othello was the victim not only of Iago's evil _____ but also of his own jealous nature.

SYNONYMS: plot, maneuver

18. mesmerize
(mez′ mə rīz)

(*v.*) to hypnotize, entrance; to fascinate, enthrall, bewitch

The magician was able to _____ the audience with his fast-moving hands and distracting chatter.

19. opprobrium
(ə prō′ brē əm)

(*n.*) disgrace arising from shameful conduct; contempt, reproach

Despite the passage of centuries, _____ is still attached to the name of the traitor Benedict Arnold.

SYNONYMS: infamy, dishonor, odium
ANTONYMS: acclaim, honor, glory, renown

20. putative
(pyü′ tə tiv)

(*adj.*) generally regarded as such; reputed; hypothesized, inferred

Ancient Celtic rituals and ceremonies are the _____ origins of some of our modern Halloween customs.

SYNONYMS: supposed, presumed
ANTONYMS: corroborated, confirmed

Choosing the Right Word

Select the **boldface** word that better completes each sentence. You might refer to the selection on pages 164–165 to see how most of these words are used in context.

1. Workers dismantled and cleaned parts of the Parthenon's exterior (**affront, facade**) during recent restoration work on the temple.

2. The audience was so quiet after the curtain fell that I couldn't tell whether they were bored or (**deigned, mesmerized**) by her artistry.

3. Philologists believe that many Western languages can be traced back to a (**putative, decorous**) parent tongue known as Indo-European.

Built in the fifth century BC, the Parthenon in Athens endures as a lasting symbol of the glory of ancient Greece.

4. A government that fails to create reform (**engenders, deigns**) the social unrest that makes violent revolution inevitable.

5. In my youthful folly, I inadvertently (**affronted, engendered**) the very people whose aid I was attempting to enlist.

6. The President must always be on his toes because a careless answer to a (**contrite, captious**) question could land him in political hot water.

7. It wasn't at all hard to recognize signs of extreme uneasiness beneath her (**canard, facade**) of buoyant optimism.

8. His unmistakable interest in the gruesome details of the tragedy revealed that he possessed the sensibilities of a (**canard, ghoul**).

9. Her quiet speech, subdued clothes, and (**decorous, desiccated**) manner made it hard to believe that she was a famous rock star.

10. "Do we have sufficient evidence at hand," I asked, "to judge the (**efficacy, cognizance**) of the new method of teaching reading?"

11. It has been said that humor is essentially the yoking of (**incongruous, ethereal**) elements within a familiar or recognizable framework.

12. For any actor, it is a unique thrill to know that when you are alone on stage, you are the (**facade, cynosure**) of hundreds of pairs of eyes.

13. If you had listened to my warnings in the first place, there would be no need for you to feel (**contrite, desiccated**) now.

14. I resent your nasty question about whether or not I will "(**deign, affront**) to speak to ordinary students" after I'm elected class president.

15. He acts like someone whose vital juices have long since dried up, leaving only a drab and (**desiccated, contrite**) shell behind.

16. The (**efficacy, opprobrium**) of history forever attaches itself to the name of Lee Harvey Oswald, the assassin of President Kennedy.

17. The book describes in great detail the odious (**machinations, facades**) involved in Adolf Hitler's rise to power in Germany.

18. The candidate's "shocking revelation" about his opponent was later shown to be nothing more than a malicious (**canard, cynosure**).

19. The play is so peopled with spirits and other incorporeal beings that it has the (**ethereal, captious**) quality of a dream.

20. He tried to conceal his lack of scholarship and intellectual depth by using unnecessarily (**efficacious, abstruse**) language.

21. Like many people who are completely wrapped up in themselves, she simply isn't (**cognizant, decorous**) of the larger world around her.

22. The daring feats of the acrobats on the high wire completely (**engendered, mesmerized**) everyone in the crowd.

23. The 1938 radio broadcast by Orson Welles that described a Martian invasion is on many lists of the greatest (**canards, efficacies**) of the twentieth century.

24. Sitting in the back of the cathedral, I strained to hear the lovely, (**ethereal, desiccated**) voices of the children wafting down from the choir loft.

25. Guests at the formal reception exhibited (**putative, decorous**) behavior.

Synonyms

*Choose the word from this unit that is the same or most nearly the same in meaning as the **boldface** word or expression in the phrase. Write that word on the line. Use a dictionary if necessary.*

1. a **fiendish** interest in death _____

2. the **parched** desert landscape _____

3. **esoteric** concepts developed by experts _____

4. **stooped** to give a few interviews _____

5. **conscious** of our mutual responsibilities _____

6. disliked for his **nit-picking** tendencies _____

7. foiled the **schemes** of the villain _____

8. **begets** mistrust by covering up mistakes _____

9. brought **shame** on the whole family _____

10. the **jarring** reunion of longtime rivals _____

Antonyms

*Choose the word from this unit that is most nearly opposite in meaning to the **boldface** word or expression in the phrase. Write that word on the line. Use a dictionary if necessary.*

1. the **unrepentant** ringleaders of the riot   _____

2. looked over the **soggy** farmland   _____

3. the **unseemly** appearance of the judge   _____

4. the **known** whereabouts of the fugitive   _____

5. the **angelic** statue   _____

Completing the Sentence

From the words in this unit, choose the one that best completes each of the following sentences. Write the word in the space provided.

1. There is little evidence that supports the idea that poverty tends to _____ poor language skills.

2. The only surefire way to establish the _____ of a new drug in treating a disease is to test it "in the field."

3. His fantastic stories about his academic, athletic, financial, and romantic achievements are a(n) _____ to common sense.

4. Except for a balcony built during the Truman administration, the _____ of the White House has remained virtually unchanged since it was constructed.

5. No one knows for sure who really wrote the scene, but Shakespeare is generally regarded as its _____ author.

6. Some historians question whether Benedict Arnold really deserves all the _____ he has been accorded as America's arch-traitor.

7. At the risk of appearing a trifle _____, I would like to raise a few small objections to the wording of this proposal.

8. Some teachers are able to present the most _____ subjects in terms that are clear to all students.

9. I didn't really believe that he was sorry for what he had done until I saw the _____ expression on his face.

10. The cherubic faces and _____ voices of the choristers almost moved me to tears.

11. Only a thoroughly naive and gullible person would actually believe every preposterous _____ that circulates in this school.

12. What could be more _____ than the 6-foot, 7-inch center on the basketball team dolled up in baby clothes for the class play!

13. The longer I study this country's history, the more _____ I become of my rich heritage of freedom.

14. The child's conduct during the ceremony may not have been appropriately _____, but it wasn't horrendous either.

15. After the battle, camp followers began the _____ process of stripping the dead of whatever valuables they possessed.

16. The _____ of the unscrupulous wheeler-dealers involved in that unsavory scandal boggle the imagination.

17. The pages of the old book were so _____ that they began to crumble as soon as we touched them.

18. To be the _____ of all eyes could be the joyous fulfillment of a dream or the unhappy realization of a nightmare.

19. For more than five minutes she stared at the telegram containing the bad news, as if she were _____.

20. Am I supposed to feel honored simply because that arrogant lout sometimes _____ to nod vaguely in my direction?

Writing: Words in Action

1. Look back at "More Than Just a Pretty Face" (pages 164–165). Suppose you have been hired by a publishing company to promote an upcoming biography of Hedy Lamarr. Write a press release to interest people in Lamarr's life and persuade them to buy the book. Use at least two details from the essay and three unit words.

2. Today it seems that cordless and wireless phones are a commonplace—if not a necessity—in the daily lives of many Americans. Think about the positive and negative consequences that these devices have had on modern life. Write an expository essay of at least three paragraphs in which you analyze the pros and cons of cell phones. Support your ideas with specific details and examples from personal experience or observations, as well as information you have gained from your own reading or media viewing. Use three or more words from this unit in your essay.

Vocabulary in Context

Literary Text

The following excerpts are from Jane Austen's novels Emma, Sense and Sensibility, *and* Pride and Prejudice. *Some of the words you have studied in this unit appear in* **boldface** *type. Complete each statement below the excerpt by circling the letter of the correct answer.*

1. The consciousness of having done amiss, had exposed her to a thousand inquietudes, and made her **captious** and irritable to a degree that must have been—that had been—hard for him to bear. (*Emma*)

   A person who is **captious**

   a. appears passive
   b. finds fault readily
   c. acts impetuously
   d. refuses to speak

2. Was it new for anything in this world to be unequal, inconsistent, **incongruous**—or for chance and circumstance (as second causes) to direct the human fate? (*Emma*)

   Something **incongruous** is

   a. inflexible
   b. misunderstood
   c. unsuitable
   d. unpredictable

3. But I had no inclination for the law, even in this less **abstruse** study of it, which my family approved. (*Sense and Sensibility*)

   Something that is **abstruse** is NOT

   a. precise
   b. expensive
   c. serious
   d. simple

4. "Could he expect that her friends would not step forward? Could he expect to be noticed again by the regiment, after such an **affront** to Colonel Forster? His temptation is not adequate to the risk!" (*Pride and Prejudice*)

   An **affront** is a(n)

   a. embarrassment
   b. act of generosity
   c. lie
   d. insult

A scene from the 2005 film version of *Pride and Prejudice*, with Brenda Blethyn, Talulah Riley, Jena Malone, and Keira Knightley

5. "And so ended his affection," said Elizabeth impatiently. "There has been many a one, I fancy, overcome in the same way. I wonder who first discovered the **efficacy** of poetry in driving away love!" (*Pride and Prejudice*)

   Poetry's **efficacy** is its

   a. mixture of rhythm and rhyme
   b. layers of meaning
   c. power to produce a desired result
   d. capacity to stir emotions

Interactive Quiz

Snap the code, or go to **vocabularyworkshop.com**

*Read the following selection, taking note of the **boldface** words and their contexts. These words are among those you will be studying in Unit 14. As you complete the exercises in this unit, it may help to refer to the way the words are used below.*

Artificial Intelligence and Social Robots

<Technical Essay>

Robots are machines programmed to interact with their surroundings. They can be stationary or mobile. They can be stand-alone systems or "insects" in a fleet. Some robots perform household chores or provide entertainment, but the most common are industrial robots **consigned** to assembly lines and service robots used for repetitive tasks such as milking cows. Some critics complain that the use of industrial and service robots can foster unemployment. Proponents claim the use of robots frees human workers from tedious physical labor that many are **loath** to do, enabling people to do more satisfying work.

The term "robot" appeared for the first time in a 1920 fantasy play by Karel Capek, and comes from a Czech word meaning "forced labor." In Capek's **visionary** tale, robots develop self-awareness, tire of servitude, and stage a **coup** that destroys the human race.

Of course, most scientists would be skeptical and **gainsay** claims about the **imminent** threat of robots rebelling against humanity. However, the notion that robots might learn to think for themselves can no longer be treated as an impossibility.

Robotics developed with **febrile** intensity in the 1990s, following advances in the field of artificial intelligence. The breakthroughs improved computer systems' capacity to perform tasks involving perception, speech recognition, decision-making, translation, and related skills. Early attempts to design intelligent robots focused on simple interactions with the environment, like getting a machine to learn to navigate down a hallway. With time, scientists began to produce robots that perceive subtle features of the world around them, even distinguishing **cacophonous** laughter from harmonious singing. Recent efforts have focused on robots that cooperate with humans by using realistic social behaviors. These "social robots" engage in interactive behaviors and respond to human actions. Some even interpret emotions normally **manifest** only to humans and make appropriate responses, including facial expressions.

In order to make interaction with social robots feel natural, many are designed to look like humans, animals, or cartoon-like characters. One Korean-made robot, modeled after famed scientist Albert

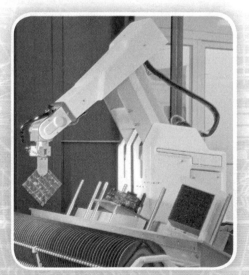

A robot completes repetitive tasks at a solar cell manufacturer.

The robot Alex Hubo was made to look like Albert Einstein.

two cameras housed in its eyes. The Einstein robot has learned to mimic a range of facial expressions, from a **beatific** smile to a wide-eyed look of surprise.

Researchers are exploring a variety of potential uses for social robots. Autism patients whose **innate** ability to interpret emotions is impaired might benefit from interaction with social robots. Emotionally responsive robots could provide companionship for the elderly and help them operate digital devices. Law-enforcement robots could help police by detecting concealed weapons and bombs. They could even take measurements of heart rate, respiration, and body temperature to recognize the **chicanery** of a lying suspect.

Some researchers and entrepreneurs claim that social robots will soon provide a **nostrum** for a range of socioeconomic ills. It is more likely that decades of research will be required before social robots have a deep impact on human life and work. However long it takes, it is clear that the die is cast. Intelligent social robots are destined to become increasingly integrated into human society.

Einstein, has a rubber face shaped to resemble the **wizened** old physicist in his later years. Designers took great pains to make the face lifelike, down to **minutiae** like a bushy mustache, fuzzy eyebrows, and gleaming eyes. Beneath its familiar appearance, the robot contains sophisticated artificial intelligence software, 32 motors to guide facial movements, and

Snap the code, or go to **vocabularyworkshop.com**

Georgia Tech University developed this social robot named Simon.

Definitions

Note the spelling, pronunciation, part(s) of speech, and definition(s) of each of the following words. Then write the word in the blank spaces in the illustrative sentence(s) following. Finally, study the lists of synonyms and antonyms.

1. beatific
(bē ə tif′ ik)

(*adj.*) blissful; rendering or making blessed

During the awards ceremony, the gold medal winner had a positively _____ expression on her face.

SYNONYMS: rapturous, ecstatic
ANTONYMS: disconsolate, dejected, doleful

2. behemoth
(bi hē′ məth)

(*n.*) a creature of enormous size, power, or appearance

The Loch Ness monster is a famous _____.

SYNONYMS: whale, elephant, colossus
ANTONYMS: dwarf, pygmy, midget

3. blandishment
(blan′ dish mənt)

(*n., often pl.*) anything designed to flatter or coax; sweet talk, apple-polishing

The king was often influenced by subtle

_____.

SYNONYMS: allurement, cajolery
ANTONYM: intimidation

4. cacophonous
(kə käf′ ə nəs)

(*adj.*) harsh-sounding, raucous, discordant, dissonant

The scene opened with _____ laughter coming from three witches gathered around a steaming cauldron.

ANTONYMS: harmonious, melodious, mellifluous

5. chicanery
(shi kā′ nə rē)

(*n.*) trickery, deceptive practices or tactics, double-dealing

The accountants used legal _____ to cover up the company's shaky financial position.

ANTONYM: fair dealing

6. consign
(kən sīn′)

(*v.*) to give over to another's care, charge, or control; to entrust, deliver; to set apart for a special use

The ship's captain _____ many duties to her trusted first mate.

SYNONYMS: remit, convey

7. coup
(kü)

(*n.*) a highly successful stroke, masterstroke, tour de force, act, plan, or stratagem; a sudden takeover of power or leadership

The surprise _____ by high-ranking military officers toppled the weak government in a matter of hours.

ANTONYMS: blunder, faux pas, gaffe

8. euphemism
(yü' fə miz əm)

(*n.*) a mild or inoffensive expression used in place of a harsh or unpleasant one; a substitute

Common _____ for *die* include the expressions *pass away* and *go to the other side*.

9. febrile
(feb' ril)

(*adj.*) feverish; pertaining to or marked by fever; frenetic

The journalist wrote with _____ intensity.

ANTONYM: leisurely

10. gainsay
(gān' sā)

(*v.*) to deny, contradict, controvert; to dispute, oppose

Some wished to _____ the conclusions of the United States Supreme Court in the matter of the 2000 presidential election.

ANTONYMS: confirm, corroborate, support, admit

11. imminent
(im' ə nənt)

(*adj.*) about to happen, threatening

An _____ hurricane forced the islanders back to the mainland.

SYNONYM: looming
ANTONYMS: distant, remote, faraway

12. innate
(i nāt')

(*adj.*) natural, inborn, inherent; built-in

Musical excellence often comes from _____ ability.

SYNONYM: congenital
ANTONYMS: learned, acquired, extrinsic, accidental

13. loath
(lōth)

(*adj.*) unwilling, reluctant, disinclined

My hard-working grandfather was _____ to retire.

SYNONYMS: averse, indisposed
ANTONYMS: eager, inclined

14. manifest
(man' ə fest)

(*adj.*) clear, evident to the eyes or mind; (*v.*) to show plainly, exhibit, evince; (*n.*) a list of cargo and/or passengers

It was _____ to many nineteenth-century Americans that the nation was destined to extend to the Pacific Ocean.

When the man began to _____ signs of hearing loss, he went to a specialist.

The passenger _____ helps investigators find out who is on board a plane.

SYNONYMS: (*adj.*) apparent; (*v.*) reveal, disclose
ANTONYMS: (*adj.*) unrevealed, hidden; (*v.*) hide, conceal

15. minutiae
(mə nü′ shē ə)

(*pl. n.*) small or trivial details, trifling matters

Because the researcher was too concerned with
_____, she was unlikely to make an
original discovery.

SYNONYM: trifles
ANTONYM: essentials

16. moratorium
(môr ə tōr′ ē əm)

(*n.*) a suspension of activity; an official waiting period; an
authorized period of delay

The conference was held to try to negotiate a
_____ on arms sales to both sides of
the conflict.

SYNONYMS: postponement, stoppage
ANTONYM: escalation

17. nostrum
(näs′ trəm)

(*n.*) an alleged cure-all; a remedy or scheme of questionable
effectiveness

The federal Food and Drug Administration was created in
part to keep unsavory characters from peddling
_____ to the public.

SYNONYM: elixir

18. pariah
(par ī′ ə)

(*n.*) one who is rejected by a social group or organization

In most of the world today, those who are suffering from the
disease of leprosy are no longer treated as

_____.

SYNONYMS: untouchable, persona non grata

19. visionary
(vizh′ ə ner ē)

(*adj.*) not practical, lacking in realism; having the nature of a
fantasy or dream; (*n.*) one given to far-fetched ideas; a dreamer
or seer characterized by vision or foresight

Ideas that once were considered _____
often become widely accepted over time.

The Reverend Martin Luther King, Jr., was a
_____ whose dreams inspired the
American civil rights movement.

SYNONYMS: (*adj.*) utopian, idealistic, impractical
ANTONYM: (*adj.*) practical

20. wizened
(wiz′ ənd)

(*adj., part.*) dry, shrunken, and wrinkled (often as the result
of aging)

The _____ old woman walked with the
aid of a cane.

SYNONYMS: withered, shriveled
ANTONYMS: bloated, distended

Choosing the Right Word

Select the **boldface** word that better completes each sentence. You might refer to the selection on pages 174–175 to see how most of these words are used in context.

1. Many scientists view Nicolaus Copernicus as a (**visionary, nostrum**), not simply a talented mathematician and the founder of modern astronomy.

2. The (**wizened, febrile**) tempo of the symphony's opening movement gives way to a placid and stately largo in the next.

3. "How much of a chance do you suppose a 98-pound weakling like me actually stands against that 320-pound (**coup, behemoth**)?" I asked incredulously.

4. (**Imminent, Loath**) disaster stared us in the face when we were thrown for a loss and then fumbled the ball on our own five-yard line.

In the sixteenth century, Copernicus concluded that the planets revolve around the sun.

5. It didn't make me any happier to learn that my firing was being referred to (**euphemistically, cacophonously**) as a "termination."

6. The (**cacophony, moratorium**) that suddenly greeted my ears made me suspect that a fox had somehow gotten into the henhouse.

7. No one who knows the facts would venture to (**gainsay, consign**) your claim to have done your utmost to improve this community.

8. Only when we tried to implement the plan did its (**innate, imminent**) defects become clear to us.

9. Although I play a fair game of chess, I'm not capable of the brilliant (**coups, manifests**) that mark a true master of the game.

10. Someone who "can't see the forest for the trees" is usually too concerned with (**minutiae, nostrums**) to be aware of the overall picture.

11. When he took his first bite of Mother's famous coconut custard pie, a look of (**visionary, beatific**) joy spread over his face.

12. Accidents at nuclear power plants have prompted some people to agitate for a (**moratorium, nostrum**) on the construction of such facilities.

13. After he killed Alexander Hamilton in a duel, Aaron Burr found himself no longer a respected statesman, but a social and political (**coup, pariah**).

14. Although I am (**febrile, loath**) to boast, I must acknowledge my superior qualities as a student, athlete, financier, and all-round social luminary.

15. "The evidence that we will present in this trial," the prosecutor told the jury, "will make the defendant's guilt abundantly (**beatific, manifest**)."

16. After it had been left to rot in the sun for a few days, the plump little apple began to take on the (**visionary, wizened**) appearance of a prune.

17. It is a rare leader indeed who can tell the public unpleasant truths without evasions or (**pariahs, blandishments**).

18. The solution to our problems is to be found in long-term programs of social planning, not in easy (**pariahs, nostrums**).

19. The plan is certainly ingenious, but it strikes me as far too (**visionary, imminent**) to serve as the basis for practical legislation.

20. "As soon as we received the order," I said, "we crated the equipment and (**gainsaid, consigned**) it to the buyer in Atlanta."

21. The kind of financial (**minutiae, chicanery**) involved in bringing off that deal may not have been illegal, but it was certainly unethical.

22. I discovered my grandfather's name on the (**moratorium, manifest**) of a ship that carried immigrants from Italy to Boston in 1919.

23. In September 1973, President Salvador Allende of Chile was ousted in a (**coup, blandishment**) organized by the military.

24. "Does anybody dare to (**manifest, gainsay**) my decision to paint the house orange?" Uncle Max inquired with a twinkle in his eye.

25. After touching the baby's (**febrile, imminent**) cheek, Harry called the doctor.

Synonyms

*Choose the word from this unit that is the same or most nearly the same in meaning as the **boldface** word or expression in the phrase. Write that word on the line. Use a dictionary if necessary.*

1. open to the **enticement** of lobbyists _____

2. a **replacement** for the word *ugly* _____

3. prepared for the **delay** _____

4. considered an **outcast** by her neighbors _____

5. when **mammoths** roamed the Earth _____

6. warned of an **impending** investigation _____

7. **transcendent** vision of another world _____

8. fascinated by the **trivia** of celebrity gossip _____

9. **transferred** to an underground facility _____

10. an **intrinsic** capacity for learning _____

Antonyms

*Choose the word from this unit that is most nearly opposite in meaning to the **boldface** word or expression in the phrase. Write that word on the line. Use a dictionary if necessary.*

1. demanded an immediate **acceleration** _____

2. a **realistic** blueprint for change _____

3. **threats** from one's enemies _____

4. was **willing** to make a compromise _____

5. looked like a **miniature** _____

Completing the Sentence

From the words in this unit, choose the one that best completes each of the following sentences. Write the word in the space provided.

1. If you spend all your time on _____, you won't have any left for really important matters.

2. Suddenly I was overcome by such a feeling of _____ peace that I began to wonder whether I was still on earth.

3. Before you dismiss him as just another impractical _____, think of how many great inventors were once regarded as mere "cranks."

4. Though her body had become bent and _____ with age, her mind was as alert and active as ever.

5. Some Civil War generals weren't professional soldiers and got their jobs through pulling strings and other forms of political _____.

6. Some people enjoy the type of atonal music written by such composers as Arnold Schoenberg; others find it _____.

7. Only a fool would have succumbed to the cloying _____ of that smooth-talking rascal!

8. However much I may dispute your views, I will never _____ your right to hold them.

9. When it became clear just how shamelessly he had treated his brother, he became a virtual _____ in his own family.

10. On the first play, our diminutive quarterback was "sacked" by a veritable _____ of a linebacker, ominously nicknamed "Bone Crusher."

11. Since I was brought up in a sleepy country town, I found it very hard to adjust to the _____ pace of big-city life.

12. We were all surprised that someone with the reputation of a frivolous playboy could _____ such courage and determination.

13. No matter what _____ you use to describe his conduct, you can't disguise the fact he betrayed his best friend.

14. Just when it seemed that defeat was inevitable, she pulled off a dazzling _____ that totally discomfited her opponent.

15. You may be, as you say, "_____ to leave such a fascinating book," but I'm telling you right now to take out the garbage!

16. In a touching ceremony, the soldiers _____ the body of their fallen leader to the grave and his memory to their hearts.

17. Though the ability to paint is probably a(n) _____ gift, it can certainly be improved by training and practice.

18. When the swollen river threatened to overflow its banks, a devastating flood seemed _____.

19. One way to bring relief to small farmers who cannot meet their mortgage payments is to declare a temporary _____ on foreclosures.

20. The nation's economic ills call for a variety of remedies; they cannot be cured by any single, miraculous _____.

Writing: Words in Action

1. Look back at "Artificial Intelligence and Social Robots" (pages 174–175). Imagine you work for a company that designs and manufactures social robots. Your task is to write an editorial that first educates the public about the nature of social robots and then explains the ways in which their use will improve the lives of many people. Use at least two details from the essay and three unit words.

2. Today, some analysts argue that the growing use of robots and other forms of automation will have a negative long-term impact on unemployment. Others claim that the use of robots will free more workers from menial and repetitive jobs and will result in an increase in satisfying jobs for highly skilled technicians and other specialists. In a brief essay, explain your viewpoint on this issue. Support your ideas with specific examples from your studies, the reading (pages 174–175), or personal observations and experience. Write at least three paragraphs, and use three or more words from this unit.

Vocabulary in Context

Literary Text

The following excerpts are from F. Scott Fitzgerald's novel **The Beautiful and Damned.** *Some of the words you have studied in this unit appear in* **boldface** *type. Complete each statement below the excerpt by circling the letter of the correct answer.*

1. After his decision a gradual improvement was **manifest.** He had taken at least a step in the direction to which hope pointed, and he realized that the less he brooded upon her the better he would be able to give the desired impression when they met.

If an improvement is **manifest**, it is
a. evident
b. anticipated
c. fleeting
d. astonishing

2. It had seemed at the time that they were always having company—she had indulged in an unspoken conviction that each guest was ever afterward slightly indebted to her. They owed her a sort of moral ten dollars apiece, and should she ever be in need she might, so to speak, borrow from them this **visionary** currency.

Something that is **visionary** is NOT
a. worthless
b. common
c. forgettable
d. practical

In the four novels and many short stories he wrote before his death in 1940, F. Scott Fitzgerald depicted the optimism and the excesses of the Jazz Age.

3. The argument faded off, but reoccurred to Anthony several times thereafter. It was disturbing to find this old belief, evidently assimilated from her mother, inserting itself again under its immemorial disguise as an **innate** idea.

An idea that is **innate** is
a. novel
b. inborn
c. hackneyed
d. indisputable

4. It seemed a tragedy to want nothing—and yet he wanted something, something. He knew in flashes what it was—some path of hope to lead him toward what he thought was an **imminent** and ominous old age.

Something that is **imminent** is
a. extremely destructive
b. lacking in energy
c. full of sadness
d. about to happen

5. Just before the engagement was announced Anthony had gone up to Tarrytown to see his grandfather, who, a little more **wizened** and grizzly as time played its ultimate chuckling tricks, greeted the news with profound cynicism.

A **wizened** person is
a. shrunken and wrinkled
b. solemn and serious
c. drowsy and forgetful
d. outspoken and loud

Interactive Quiz

Snap the code, or go to **vocabularyworkshop.com**

*Read the following selection, taking note of the **boldface** words and their contexts. These words are among those you will be studying in Unit 15. As you complete the exercises in this unit, it may help to refer to the way the words are used below.*

Private Life in the Public Eye

<Humorous Essay>

There are many reasons to keep a private diary. Jotting down your thoughts helps you sort out **nascent** feelings. Sketching plans helps you make way toward your goals. Whatever your reasons, keeping a diary is a perfect way to exercise your **inviolable** right to take yourself too seriously. The only problem is, it's hard to keep your private scribblings safe from prying eyes. To keep a diary is to run the risk that your secret thoughts might be discovered by some snooping relative or friend, even **promulgated** round the world, like the evening news or the latest scandal on the Internet.

One of history's great examples of private thoughts gone public is a diary penned in the seventeenth century by Samuel Pepys (1633–1703). Pepys was an ambitious man who climbed the ranks of English society by skillful work and diligent networking, eventually becoming a member of Parliament, a Fellow of the Royal Society, and Secretary for the Admiralty. On account of his public achievements, we should consider him a leading man of his day. But the diary he left to his **progeny**, having slipped into the records of history, provides another **aperture** through which to view the man.

Visscher's view of London, 1616

In the pages of his private thoughts, Pepys, for all his hard work, high culture, and dignified connections, seems a man of **restive** habits and **mutable** character. He wrestles with his vices in his diary, time and again falling short of moral **rectitude** and raking over the ashes of his chief **iniquities**: his **epicurean** love of wine, his addiction to the theater, and his lust for women other than his wife.

To the historian, Pepys's diary provides an insider's glimpse of the English Restoration: meetings with the king and other men of high office, eyewitness accounts of the Great Fire and the Great Plague of London, and views on the politics of war and peace. But the casual reader—who might not care a **pittance** for international affairs of the seventeenth century—is more apt to enjoy the diary's personal anecdotes. Mr. Pepys rolls over one night in his sleep accidentally to smash his wife in the nose with his elbow.

Another evening, he's threatening to fling her poor dog out the window. For months on end he's racked with jealousy, afraid his wife might have an eye for other men, though he doesn't let the sentiment interfere with his own thoughts on comely women. He criticizes the king's skill at tennis, reports on the monarch's drinking habits and mistresses, and complains about the flatterers who praise their ruler far more than he deserves.

For all the notable accomplishments of his public life, Samuel Pepys is most commonly remembered as a funny fellow who kept a diary and who could not **subsist** without wine, plays, or the other **amenities** of his times. His honesty and enthusiasm for the details of his life might be worth a **panegyric**, but for some of his flaws the man deserves to be **pilloried**. We would know nothing of his shortcomings if it weren't for the **improvident** decision, or perhaps the odd pride, that led Pepys to leave his diary behind. On the other hand, if it weren't for that diary, most of us would not know the man at all. This very public legacy is a reminder to anyone who aspires to be a "private" diarist. Be careful what you commit to print!

King Charles II was the subject of many of Pepys's diary entries.

iWords

Snap the code, or go to
vocabularyworkshop.com

Definitions

Note the spelling, pronunciation, part(s) of speech, and definition(s) of each of the following words. Then write the word in the blank spaces in the illustrative sentence(s) following. Finally, study the lists of synonyms and antonyms.

1. amenity
(ə men′ ə tē)

(*n.*) that which is pleasant or agreeable; (*pl.*) attractive features, customs, etc.

When I backpack, there are certain basic

_____, such as hot meals and a dry tent, that I will not go without.

ANTONYMS: unpleasantness, disagreeableness

2. aperture
(ap′ ər chər)

(*n.*) an opening, gap, hole; orifice

After the earthquake, rain and cold came through the

_____ in the wall of the damaged house.

ANTONYMS: closure, blockage, occlusion

3. dissidence
(dis′ ə dəns)

(*n.*) a difference of opinion; discontent

When the commanding officer announced that all leave was cancelled, there was widespread _____ in the ranks.

SYNONYMS: disagreement, disaffection
ANTONYMS: harmony, concord

4. epicurean
(ep ə kyü′ rē ən)

(*adj.*) devoted to the pursuit of pleasure; fond of good food, comfort, and ease; with discriminating tastes; (*n.*) a person with discriminating tastes

The chef took an _____ delight in presenting the most delicious dishes to his demanding clientele.

Even the most fervent _____ should not expect fine dining in a poor, war-torn country.

SYNONYMS: (*adj.*) sybaritic, discriminating
ANTONYMS: (*adj.*) ascetic, self-denying, abstemious

5. improvident
(im präv′ ə dənt)

(*adj.*) not thrifty; failing to plan ahead

Some people are so _____ that despite high incomes they struggle to make ends meet.

SYNONYMS: prodigal, spendthrift, extravagant
ANTONYMS: frugal, economical, cautious

6. iniquity
(i nik′ wə tē)

(*n.*) wickedness, sin; a grossly immoral act

English Puritans looked upon the court that surrounded King Charles I as a den of _____.

SYNONYMS: evil, crime
ANTONYMS: probity, rectitude, uprightness

7. inviolable
(in vī' ə lə bəl)

(*adj.*) sacred; of such a character that it must not be broken, injured, or profaned

Safeguarding the retirement income of millions of Americans is an _____ trust of the federal government.

SYNONYM: unassailable
ANTONYMS: vulnerable, assailable

8. mutable
(myü' tə bəl)

(*adj.*) open to or capable of change, fickle

Most people would agree that one's principles and moral values should not be as _____ as fashion.

SYNONYMS: changeable, variable
ANTONYMS: changeless, steadfast, constant

9. nascent
(nā' sənt)

(*adj.*) just beginning to exist or develop; having just come into existence

Recent public opinion polls registered _____ opposition to the proposed tax increase.

SYNONYMS: incipient, embryonic
ANTONYMS: dying, moribund, senescent

10. obeisance
(ō bē' səns)

(*n.*) a deep bow or other body movement indicating respect or submission; deference, homage

Upon entering the throne room, each courtier made a respectful _____ before the king and queen.

SYNONYM: honor
ANTONYMS: disrespect, irreverence

11. panegyric
(pan ə ji' rik)

(*n.*) formal or elaborate praise; a tribute

The speaker delivered a _____ in honor of the award-winning author.

SYNONYMS: tribute, encomium, testimonial
ANTONYMS: tirade, philippic

12. pillory
(pil' ə rē)

(*n.*) a device for publicly punishing offenders; a means for exposing one to public contempt or ridicule; (*v.*) to expose to public contempt or ridicule

The _____ was placed in the center of town so that everyone could view the outlaws and their shame.

The candidate tried to _____ her political opponent by suggesting that he had ties to organized crime.

ANTONYMS: (*v.*) extol, laud, acclaim

13. pittance
(pit′ əns)

(*n.*) a woefully meager allowance, wage, or portion
In comparison to the overwhelming need for food and medicine, the shipment was a mere _____.
SYNONYM: trifle; ANTONYM: fortune

14. presage
(pres′ ij)

(*v.*) to foreshadow or point to a future event; to predict; (*n.*) a warning or indication of the future
The skirmishes at the border _____ a war.
The fall in stock prices and retail sales may be a
_____ of hard economic times to come.
SYNONYMS: (*v.*) augur, foretell

15. progeny
(präj′ ə nē)

(*n.*) descendants, offspring, children, followers, disciples
The Bill of Rights guarantees certain civil rights and protections to us and our _____.
SYNONYMS: issue, posterity; ANTONYMS: forebears, antecedents

16. promulgate
(präm′ əl gāt)

(*v.*) to proclaim or issue officially; to make known far and wide
The School Board _____ a new approach to education that emphasized phonics.
SYNONYM: announce
ANTONYMS: withdraw, retract, abrogate, nullify

17. rectitude
(rek′ tə tüd)

(*n.*) uprightness, righteousness; correctness
The mayor is a person of unquestionable
_____.
SYNONYMS: probity, integrity
ANTONYMS: iniquity, heinousness

18. restive
(res′ tiv)

(*adj.*) restless, hard to manage, balky
The _____ horse had not been taken out of the stable for five days.
SYNONYMS: uneasy, recalcitrant
ANTONYMS: serene, unruffled, docile

19. seraphic
(sə raf′ ik)

(*adj.*) angelic, heavenly, celestial
The artist painted the children with _____ smiles to suggest their innocence.
SYNONYM: cherubic; ANTONYMS: devilish

20. subsist
(səb sist′)

(*v.*) to have existence; to remain alive, manage to make a living or maintain life; to persist or continue
Peasants in nineteenth-century Ireland were able to
_____ almost exclusively on potatoes.
SYNONYMS: last, sustain

Choosing the Right Word

*Select the **boldface** word that better completes each sentence. You might refer to the selection on pages 184–185 to see how most of these words are used in context.*

1. Petty criminals in medieval England were often placed in stocks or (**progeny, pillories**) and subjected to public humiliation.

2. There was a loophole in the law, and through this (**aperture, obeisance**) the defendant escaped the legal consequences of his crime.

3. Religious (**obeisance, dissidence**) was one of the motives that led many people to found colonies in North America.

An offender sentenced to the stocks had his feet, head, or hands locked in a heavy wooden frame.

4. The novel centers on a(n) (**improvident, seraphic**) young man who squanders his inheritance and dies in the poorhouse.

5. Like so many others of his generation, he paid unquestioning (**iniquity, obeisance**) to the accepted symbols of material success.

6. The cost of living has risen so sharply that a salary that was adequate a decade ago is now no more than a mere (**panegyric, pittance**).

7. "Angelica" is indeed an apt name for one whose (**mutable, seraphic**) beauty is complemented by such sweetness of temper and gentleness of spirit.

8. Recently, the principal (**promulgated, presaged**) a new dress code that abolished some of the unnecessary strictness of the old rules.

9. Specific customs vary widely in different lands, but the basic (**apertures, amenities**) of civilized living are much the same everywhere.

10. Writers often regard their works as their (**dissidence, progeny**) in much the same way as other people regard their pets as family members.

11. The new "gourmet" deli features delicacies that are bound to delight even the most exacting of (**epicurean, nascent**) palates.

12. No matter how well defended, no boundary is (**inviolable, restive**) unless the people on either side of it respect each other.

13. Instead of being so concerned with the (**iniquities, apertures**) of others, they would do well to concentrate on correcting their own shortcomings.

14. I realize the official made a serious mistake, but that is no reason to (**pillory, subsist**) him so unmercifully in the press.

15. The resounding victory we scored at the polls is an eloquent tribute to the (**rectitude, dissidence**) of her approach as campaign manager.

16. We would like to believe that the intensifying fear of ecological catastrophe (**subsists, presages**) an era of environmental harmony in the near future.

17. Instead of mouthing empty (**panegyrics, apertures**) to the Bill of Rights, let's strive to make this great document a reality in our lives.

18. One cannot expect a(n) (**epicurean, nascent**) democracy to go through its early years without experiencing serious growing pains.

19. The study of government shows us that many political institutions thought to be unchanging are in fact highly (**inviolable, mutable**).

20. As the speaker's remarks became more inflammatory, the crowd grew more sullen and (**nascent, restive**).

21. Liberty (**subsists, presages**) only as long as people have the intelligence to know their rights and the courage to defend them.

22. I hope that Jessie's obvious nervousness during the dress rehearsal does not (**presage, promulgate**) a poor performance in the play tonight.

23. The visitors lowered their voices and made (**obeisance, iniquity**) to the distinguished gentleman who was beckoning them toward the castle entrance.

24. Grandma sighed, "Kim's taste in clothes is so (**promulgated, mutable**) that nobody even tries to guess what she'll wear from week to week."

25. (**Pittances, Amenities**) at the luxury spa include massages and steam baths.

Synonyms

*Choose the word from this unit that is the same or most nearly the same in meaning as the **boldface** word or expression in the phrase. Write that word on the line. Use a dictionary if necessary.*

1. the angry **dissent** of protestors _____

2. tried to **survive** in a desert _____

3. dark clouds that **portend** rain _____

4. a **saintly** figure dressed in white _____

5. the **sacrosanct** principle of equality _____

6. a **hedonistic** display of luxury _____

7. paid **respect** to those who came before her _____

8. repaid a mere **modicum** of what is owed _____

9. showed a **budding** interest in politics _____

10. **fidgety** after the caffeine _____

Antonyms

*Choose the word from this unit that is most nearly opposite in meaning to the **boldface** word or expression in the phrase. Write that word on the line. Use a dictionary if necessary.*

1. widespread political **agreement** _____

2. always treats those in authority with **disregard** _____

3. a puppy with an **impish** demeanor _____

4. a **thrifty** manager _____

5. insulted the king's **ancestors** _____

Completing the Sentence

From the words in this unit, choose the one that best completes each of the following sentences. Write the word in the space provided.

1. After a few days in which everything went my way, I suddenly learned just how _____ Lady Luck can be.

2. We are sure that their vow is _____ because their sense of moral obligation will prevent them from ever breaking it.

3. "I'm afraid that the child's _____ countenance belies the mischief in his heart," I observed sadly.

4. Though I'm by no means _____ with my money, I don't hoard it either.

5. The _____ on most cameras can be adjusted to admit more or less light, as required.

6. Our financial situations are so different that what she considers a mere _____ seems a fortune to me.

7. The biography is a pretty evenhanded appraisal of the man's strengths and weaknesses, not just another _____ to a great hero.

8. Nutritionists say that most of us could _____ on a great deal less food than we actually consume.

9. Conscientious parents will do everything they can to foster and develop the _____ intellectual curiosity of a small child.

10. The President has _____ a policy that commits the nation to curbing pollution.

11. The wranglers suspected that there were wolves or mountain lions nearby when the herd suddenly grew nervous and _____.

12. For many ancient peoples, the appearance of a comet was a fearful omen that _____ great social upheaval.

13. The liberties that we have inherited from our forefathers are a sacred trust that we must pass on undiminished to our _____.

14. Am I to be _____ before the entire student body because I made a few minor mistakes as a member of the Student Council?

15. The Bible tells us that visitors to the court of Solomon, the great Hebrew king, willingly paid him _____.

16. Imagine someone with my _____ tastes having to live for a week on that watery mush!

17. It was the _____ of its natural setting on those rolling hills that led the architect to dub the estate "Mount Pleasant."

18. Authoritarian governments often resort to violence and coercion in their efforts to repress political _____.

19. He inveighs against the sins of society with all the stridency of an Old Testament prophet castigating the _____ of the unworthy.

20. I see no reason to question the _____ of her dealings with us since I know her to be "as honest as the day is long."

Writing: Words in Action

1. Look back at "Private Life in the Public Eye" (pages 184–185). Think about how the experience of keeping a diary is different from the experience of composing an autobiography. Write a brief essay in which you compare and contrast those two genres and explain which kind of writing you would prefer to do. Use examples from your experience and prior knowledge to support your ideas. Include at least two details from the essay and three unit words.

2. *"What is a diary as a rule? A document useful to the person who keeps it. Dull to the contemporary who reads it and invaluable to the student, centuries afterwards, who treasures it." —attributed to Dame Ellen Terry*

What do you think about Terry's statement? Do you agree with her views about diaries? In what ways might a diary be useful to the person who keeps it? In a brief essay, support your opinion with specific examples from the reading (refer to pages 184–185), your studies, or personal experiences. Write at least three paragraphs, and use three or more words from this unit.

Vocabulary in Context

The following excerpts are from Edith Wharton's novels The Custom of the Country *and* The House of Mirth. *Some of the words you have studied in this unit appear in* **boldface** *type. Complete each statement below the excerpt by circling the letter of the correct answer.*

1. She felt no compunction in continuing to accept an undiminished allowance: it was the hereditary habit of the parent animal to despoil himself for his **progeny**. (*The Custom of the Country*)

    Progeny are

    a. principles
    b. happiness
    c. descendants
    d. ambitions

2. Paul, after Mrs. Heeny's departure, had grown fretful and **restive**, and Undine had found it more and more difficult to fit his small exacting personality into her cramped rooms and crowded life. (*The Custom of the Country*)

    Someone who is **restive** is NOT

    a. optimistic
    b. docile
    c. servile
    d. healthy

3. She wanted, passionately and persistently, two things which she believed should **subsist** together in any well-ordered life: amusement and respectability; and despite her surface-sophistication her notion of amusement was hardly less innocent than when she had hung on the plumber's fence with Indiana Frusk. (*The Custom of the Country*)

    To **subsist** is to

    a. labor
    b. exist
    c. correlate
    d. aspire

Edith Wharton wrote about New York high society in many of her novels and stories.

4. "Hallo, Selden, going too? You're an **Epicurean** like myself, I see: you don't want to see all those goddesses gobbling terrapin. Gad, what a show of good-looking women; but not one of 'em could touch that little cousin of mine." (*The House of Mirth*)

    An **epicurean**

    a. is extremely talkative
    b. fears being alone
    c. likes to take risks
    d. has refined tastes

5. Everything in her surroundings ministered to feelings of ease and **amenity**. The windows stood open to the sparkling freshness of the September morning... (*The House of Mirth*)

    An **amenity** is something that is

    a. pleasant
    b. energetic
    c. poignant
    d. hopeful

Interactive Quiz

Snap the code, or go to **vocabularyworkshop.com**

Vocabulary for Comprehension

*Read the following selection in which some of the words you have studied in Units 13–15 appear in **boldface** type. Then answer the questions on page 195.*

This passage focuses on one of the most famous American novelists of the twentieth century, F. Scott Fitzgerald.

(Line)

Few writers have been as identified with an age as F. Scott Fitzgerald (1896–1940). Not only is his best fiction set in the 1920s, but
(5) he helped define that era as the Jazz Age, an **epicurean** decade of fevered pleasure-seeking, **improvident** spending, and gaudy excess.
(10) Born in St. Paul, Minnesota, Francis Scott Key Fitzgerald (named after his famous ancestor) was a restless young man full of romantic dreams. In 1917 he left Princeton
(15) University, before receiving his degree, to train as an Army officer, but he never made it overseas. While stationed at Camp Sheridan near Montgomery, Alabama, Fitzgerald
(20) fell for a local southern beauty, Zelda Sayre. By dint of sheer charm and persistence, Fitzgerald got Zelda to agree to marry him, but she was too **cognizant** of his poverty to succumb
(25) permanently to his **blandishments**. When the novel he was writing was rejected for a second time, she broke off the engagement.

Scott, however, was not deterred.
(30) He went back to St. Paul and rewrote the novel again. Upon its

third submission to the Scribners publishing house, the manuscript was accepted. It was published in
(35) 1920 as *This Side of Paradise* and became an instant success. Scott and Zelda were married within a week. Like the characters in Fitzgerald's Jazz Age novels, the
(40) couple spent the next decade shuttling between New York and Europe, living the high life and spending lavishly. Behind the frothy **facade**, however, lay a darker reality
(45) that Fitzgerald depicted in his most famous novel, *The Great Gatsby* (1925). In *Gatsby*, Fitzgerald examines the moral decadence **engendered** by the American dream
(50) of wealth and success. When Fitzgerald died of a heart attack at the age of 44 (Zelda died in a fire only a few years later), his works that chronicled such a discrete
(55) period of American history seemed on their way to obscurity. In the 1950s, however, critics revived such classics as *Gatsby* and *Tender Is the Night* (1934), securing a place for
(60) him in the canon of American writers.

1. According to the author, which era did Fitzgerald help to define?
   a. the Information Age
   b. the Civil Rights era
   c. the Great Depression
   d. the Jazz Age
   e. the Age of Discovery

2. The meaning of **epicurean** (line 6) is
   a. idyllic
   b. uneventful
   c. hedonistic
   d. impoverished
   e. turbulent

3. **Improvident** (line 8) most nearly means
   a. frugal
   b. extravagant
   c. prudent
   d. intermittent
   e. impressive

4. In paragraph 2 (lines 10–28), it may be inferred that when Scott was courting Zelda, her values were
   a. patriotic
   b. idealistic
   c. romantic
   d. literary
   e. materialistic

5. **Cognizant** (line 24) is best defined as
   a. aware
   b. proud
   c. oblivious
   d. ashamed
   e. scornful

6. The meaning of **blandishments** (line 25) is
   a. apologies
   b. enticements
   c. fantasies
   d. threats
   e. tantrums

7. You can infer that an important factor in Scott and Zelda's marriage was
   a. his repeated pleas to her
   b. Scott's promise to leave New York
   c. the couple's admiring European friends

d. the instant success of *This Side of Paradise*
   e. the intervention of Zelda's parents

8. According to the author, the main focus in the novel *The Great Gatsby* is on which of the following?
   a. the corruption of American politics
   b. the pitfalls of romance
   c. the moral decadence flowing from the American dream
   d. the complex rhythms of jazz
   e. aspects of European society

9. **Facade** (line 44) most nearly means
   a. lifestyle
   b. costume
   c. mask
   d. attitude
   e. celebration

10. **Engendered** (line 49) most nearly means
    a. deterred
    b. generated
    c. enraged
    d. offended
    e. baffled

11. The primary purpose of the passage is to
    a. survey the highlights of Fitzgerald's life and literary career
    b. analyze contrasts between Fitzgerald's early novels and his later works
    c. support the claim that *The Great Gatsby* is Fitzgerald's masterpiece
    d. show how the Fitzgeralds epitomized the Jazz Age lifestyle
    e. emphasize the irony in Fitzgerald's handling of the theme of illusion versus reality

12. For the most part, what organizational scheme does the author use in the passage?
    a. comparison and contrast
    b. order of impression
    c. order of importance
    d. spatial order
    e. chronological order

Two-Word Completions

Select the pair of words that best complete the meaning of each of the following passages.

1. As soon as the famous movie star walked into my shop, she became the _____ of all eyes. Customers stopped what they were doing to stare at her as if _____ by the spell of her celebrity.
   a. aperture . . . engendered
   b. cynosure . . . mesmerized
   c. moratorium . . . subsisted
   d. pillory . . . promulgated

2. Disgruntled army officers and other _____ elements in the society engineered the bloody _____ that toppled the duly elected government a few months after it had taken office.
   a. contrite . . . nostrum
   b. restive . . . moratorium
   c. visionary . . . pittance
   d. dissident . . . coup

3. Once the news broke, the public heaped so much _____ on the head of the hapless city official that he soon found himself a veritable political _____, even in his own party.
   a. euphemism . . . canard
   b. dissidence . . . amenity
   c. opprobrium . . . pariah
   d. efficacy . . . ghoul

4. Behind the courtier's outward _____ of decorous sloth there lurked the _____ imagination of an inveterate opportunist, eager to capitalize on any windfall that came his way.
   a. aperture . . . incongruous
   b. facade . . . febrile
   c. cynosure . . . nascent
   d. chicanery . . . improvident

5. The characters in Jane Austen novels display _____ manners, obeying the _____ of social conventions that range from how many consecutive waltzes a couple may dance to the type of tea that should be served to guests.
   a. abstruse . . . canards
   b. ethereal . . .pariahs
   c. decorous . . . minutiae
   d. beatific . . . manifests

6. Any official who is genuinely concerned about the _____ of his or her behavior while in public office will think twice before engaging in the kinds of political _____ and backroom shenanigans that sometimes go on when a juicy government contract is up for grabs.
   a. rectitude . . . chicanery
   b. imminence . . . blandishments
   c. progeny . . . machinations
   d. iniquity . . . cognizance

7. At the demonstration in front of company headquarters, the protestor who _____ to address the media described the layoffs as a hurtful _____ to employee loyalty.
   a. consigned . . . behemoth
   b. deigned . . . affront
   c. gainsaid . . . panegyric
   d. manifested . . . obeisance

Idioms

In the essay about writer Samuel Pepys and his diary (see pages 184–185), the author describes Pepys as "raking over the ashes" his major vices and sins. This saying is an idiom. The author means that in some diary entries Pepys returns to discuss and reflect on unpleasant events from his past.

An **idiom** is an expression that cannot be translated literally. The meaning of an idiom is not suggested by the meaning of its separate words. You learn idioms in the same way that you learn many new words—by hearing or reading them in context. If you cannot understand an idiom from context clues, you may need to use an online or print dictionary to determine or confirm its meaning.

Choosing the Right Idiom

Read each sentence. Use context clues to figure out the meaning of each idiom in **boldface** *print. Then write the letter of the definition for the idiom in the sentence.*

1. Did you actually enjoy that movie, or did you just **jump on the bandwagon** because it received three Academy Awards? _____

2. The police are **barking up the wrong tree** if they think Joey broke the windows; he has an airtight alibi for the entire evening. _____

3. The campaign manager wants Jones to remain **above the fray** when it comes to launching personal attacks on the other candidates. _____

4. When the video game was released, the developer must have made money **hand over fist**. _____

5. "I want to speak to the manager now," Melissa demanded, "so that I can get answers to all my questions **in one fell swoop**." _____

6. The employees applauded their boss for keeping them **in the loop** about possible changes to the holiday delivery schedule _____

7. After two months of tense negotiations, union leaders decided to **throw in the towel** and urged their members to go on strike. _____

8. "Because you are so **quick on the draw**," Mickey said to his best friend, "we have an excellent chance to win the obstacle race." _____

9. The high school senior won a full scholarship to the college of his choice, so he is **sitting pretty** for the next several years. _____

10. Sadly, because the investment scheme was nothing but **smoke and mirrors**, hundreds of people lost their entire savings. _____

a. rapidly and continuously

b. able to react quickly

c. trickery and deception

d. not involved in the argument or unpleasantness

e. having knowledge of something

f. believing the wrong explanation for something

g. in a good situation

h. all at once

i. admit failure or defeat

j. support something because it is popular

Writing with Idioms

Find the meaning of each idiom. (Use an online or print dictionary if necessary.) Then write a sentence for each idiom.

1. no great shakes

_____

2. bar none

_____

3. off the cuff

_____

4. my cup of tea

_____

5. stand your ground

_____

_____

6. cut the mustard

_____

_____

7. running on empty

_____

_____

8. for a song

_____

9. take the plunge

_____

10. toe the line

_____

11. out of left field

_____

12. have egg on your face

_____

Denotation and Connotation

The **denotation** of a word is its dictionary meaning or meanings. Beyond its denotations, many words may also have connotations. **Connotations** are the ideas and emotional associations that words carry apart from their denotative meanings

Denotations are objective, but connotations are subjective; they can vary from person to person. A word's connotation(s) may be *neutral*, *positive*, or *negative*.

Consider these synonyms for the neutral word *abstruse*:

abstract   profound   cryptic   unintelligible

Abstract and *profound* have neutral or positive connotations, suggesting something is difficult to understand because of its conceptual complexity or the depth and thoughtfulness of its ideas. *Cryptic* and *unintelligible*, however, suggest a difficulty in understanding based on an unfortunate obscurity or a jumbled and incoherent explanation.

> **Think:** The research of a learned and well-respected professor can be described as abstract or profound, while the work of a lesser scholar is deemed cryptic or unintelligible.

Look at these examples of words with similar denotations but different connotations.

NEUTRAL	POSITIVE	NEGATIVE
critical	discerning	captious
portion	allowance	pittance
discriminating	epicurean	self-indulgent

Distinguishing among sometimes subtle shades of meaning will help you say exactly what you mean, prevent misunderstandings, and create the tone or mood you intend.

Shades of Meaning

Write a plus sign (+) in the box if the word has a positive connotation.
Write a minus sign (–) if the word has a negative connotation. Put a zero (0)
if the word is neutral.

1. canard ☐   **2.** desiccated ☐   **3.** opprobrium ☐   **4.** putative ☐

5. engender ☐   **6.** innate ☐   **7.** pillory ☐   **8.** seraphic ☐

9. nostrum ☐   **10.** facade ☐   **11.** amenity ☐   **12.** cacophonous ☐

13. efficacy ☐   **14.** ghoulish ☐   **15.** nascent ☐   **16.** pariah ☐

Expressing the Connotation

Read each sentence. Select the word in parentheses that expresses the connotation (positive, negative, or neutral) given at the beginning of the sentence.

positive
1. The host and hostess were pleased with the (**decorous, staid**) behavior of all the party guests.

neutral
2. Were you as surprised by the (**machinations, maneuvers**) of the play's protagonist as I was?

negative
3. We couldn't believe Mike spent most of the long ride discussing the (**minutiae, features**) of his new saxophone.

negative
4. The tenant (**consigned, abandoned**) the furniture in his apartment when he moved out.

positive
5. The interview committee seemed impressed by the final job candidate's (**rectitude, disposition**).

positive
6. Upon seeing Dr. Slack enter the lobby, we hastily made an (**obeisance, acknowledgment**) to him.

negative
7. My neighbor decided for whom she would vote weeks ago, but I've learned that her political decisions are (**mutable, unstable**).

positive
8. In the foreground of the oil painting stands an elegantly dressed elderly woman with a (**beatific, supernatural**) expression on her face.

Challenge: Using Connotation

Choose vocabulary words from Units 13–15 to replace the highlighted words in the sentences below. Then explain how the connotation of the replacement word changes the tone of the sentence.

cognizant	chicanery	apertures
affronted	deigned	ethereal

1. When she first saw her costume, the actress immediately noticed how light and **flimsy** _____ it seemed.

_____

_____

2. The antique shop owner uses subtle **tactics** _____ to get customers to pay top prices for his merchandise.

_____

_____

3. The young man ahead of me in line at the airport was obviously **affected** _____ by another passenger's remark about his hair.

_____

_____

Classical Roots

vid, vis—to look, see

This root appears in **visionary** (page 178), which means "lacking in practicality" or, as a noun, "a dreamer or seer." Some other words based on this same root are listed below.

advisement	providence	proviso	visitation
envisage	provident	visage	vista

From the list of words above, choose the one that corresponds to each of the brief definitions below. Write the word in the blank space in the illustrative sentence below the definition. Use an online or print dictionary if necessary.

1. a careful consideration (*"act of seeing to"*)

The committee has agreed to take your most recent request under

_____.

2. a distinct view or prospect through an opening; an extensive mental view

As we rounded the bend, we suddenly beheld the most breathtaking

_____ of our trip.

3. to picture to oneself (*"see into"*); conceive of, especially as a future possibility

It is hard to _____ a modern America made up entirely of small farmers.

4. a face, countenance, appearance, look, aspect (*"that which is seen"*)

The links of chains he carried, which signified his sins, gave Jacob Marley a

frightening _____.

5. a conditional stipulation; an article or clause in a contract that introduces a condition (*"that which is foreseen"*)

They agreed to sign the deal, with the _____ that we serve as witnesses.

6. providing for future needs or contingencies; thrifty, economical

It is our agency's mission to explore the most _____ use of our natural resources.

7. a visit for the purpose of making an official inspection; an act of visiting; a severe punishment or affliction

Health specialists are meeting to discuss the possibility of a new

_____ of tuberculosis.

8. divine guidance or care; a manifestation of such guidance

Despite hard times, or perhaps especially during hard times, people of faith put

their trust in _____.

Synonyms

Select the two words or expressions that are most nearly the same in meaning.

1. **a.** countermand **b.** repudiate **c.** exonerate **d.** embellish
2. **a.** renovate **b.** raze **c.** pillory **d.** demolish
3. **a.** debris **b.** frenzy **c.** flotsam **d.** cabal
4. **a.** unwonted **b.** paltry **c.** insignificant **d.** beneficial
5. **a.** eulogy **b.** juggernaut **c.** critique **d.** tribute
6. **a.** object **b.** volunteer **c.** demur **d.** jettison
7. **a.** suppliant **b.** fiat **c.** decree **d.** consent
8. **a.** wretched **b.** nefarious **c.** fearless **d.** abject
9. **a.** amplify **b.** verify **c.** substantiate **d.** recant
10. **a.** sophistry **b.** desire **c.** gall **d.** effrontery
11. **a.** picayune **b.** plenary **c.** trifling **d.** irrelevant
12. **a.** overcome **b.** foreshadow **c.** portend **d.** eschew
13. **a.** echelon **b.** mandate **c.** objection **d.** authorization
14. **a.** deign **b.** stoop **c.** exhume **d.** attempt
15. **a.** deprecate **b.** decimate **c.** deplore **d.** approve

Antonyms

Select the two words that are most nearly opposite in meaning.

16. **a.** delineate **b.** arrogate **c.** renounce **d.** remain
17. **a.** intellectual **b.** moot **c.** indisputable **d.** disturbed
18. **a.** feckless **b.** disagreeable **c.** seraphic **d.** effective
19. **a.** youthful **b.** obsequious **c.** moribund **d.** thriving
20. **a.** loquacious **b.** frenetic **c.** calm **d.** vituperative
21. **a.** flatter **b.** embezzle **c.** hallow **d.** calumniate
22. **a.** restive **b.** banal **c.** original **d.** militant
23. **a.** coherent **b.** glorious **c.** wizened **d.** muddled
24. **a.** decry **b.** presage **c.** commend **d.** apportion
25. **a.** consecrate **b.** antagonize **c.** conciliate **d.** forgo

Analogies

Select the item that best completes the comparison.

26. avid is to **indifference** as
   a. germane is to appropriateness
   b. taciturn is to prolixity
   c. halcyon is to serenity
   d. substantive is to eloquence

27. brackish is to **drink** as
   a. visible is to see
   b. incendiary is to burn
   c. indigestible is to eat
   d. piquant is to whet

28. mule is to **intransigent** as
   a. monkey is to verdant
   b. fly is to acquisitive
   c. horse is to devious
   d. bat is to myopic

29. maelstrom is to **sea** as
   a. foliage is to desert
   b. quicksand is to swamp
   c. hurricane is to shower
   d. skyscraper is to forest

30. acuity is to **see** as
   a. perspicacity is to argue
   b. equity is to report
   c. sensitivity is to feel
   d. concord is to disturb

31. depraved is to **corruption** as
   a. moot is to originality
   b. frenetic is to leisure
   c. mordant is to obscurity
   d. overweening is to excess

32. derelict is to **conscientiousness** as
   a. consummate is to perfection
   b. intermittent is to continuity
   c. pecuniary is to money
   d. ubiquitous is to prevalence

33. saturnine is to **gloom** as
   a. fatuous is to intelligence
   b. macabre is to gaiety
   c. refulgent is to darkness
   d. lackadaisical is to indolence

Two-Word Completions

Select the best word pair from among the choices given.

34. I don't mean to _____ the point by telling you again, but if you don't exercise, your muscles will _____.
   a. loath . . . languish
   b. inure . . . mesmerize
   c. belabor . . . atrophy
   d. requite . . . saturate

35. His artistic choices are so strange and _____ that he runs the risk of being labeled a _____ and not being taken seriously.
   a. rife . . . canard
   b. pejorative . . . tyro
   c. abstruse . . . progeny
   d. eclectic . . . dilettante

36. It simply seems _____ to _____ someone for not throwing away a gum wrapper properly; wouldn't a warning be more appropriate?
   a. inane . . . incarcerate
   b. furtive . . . vacillate
   c. aesthetic . . . discomfit
   d. ebullient . . . congeal

37. The _____ office-holder has a decided advantage over her opponent, who has never held office and is a political _____.
   a. incumbent . . . neophyte
   b. cognizant . . . utopia
   c. visionary . . . effigy
   d. felicitous . . . penitent

Supplying Words in Context

To complete each sentence, select the best word from among the choices given. Not all words in the word bank will be used. You may modify the word form as necessary.

allay	murky	paucity	counterpart
eschew	undulate	raiment	pusillanimous
pedantry	nuance	accost	unremitting
bucolic	travesty	illusory	tenable

38. The teacher sought to _____ our concerns about the upcoming test.

39. The verdant and _____ setting was soothing in its tranquility.

40. The ocean water was so _____ that we couldn't see our feet.

41. The subtle _____ of this story will be lost on a reader who is less than attentive.

42. Our good fortune proved _____, and we were soon back in deep difficulty.

43. In order to lose weight, I will _____ fats and sweets and eat more fruits and vegetables.

carping	echelon	emulate	coterie
invidious	dissemble	stratagem	glean
jocular	enervate	gambit	mundane
garish	litany	nettle	distraught

44. The constant _____ of the children was beginning to drive the baby-sitter to her wits' end!

45. The pop singer's _____ of admirers flattered her constantly and kept her shielded from criticism.

46. Would he _____, or would he tell the truth?

47. Lucius didn't need to say a word: I could _____ from the look on his face that he wasn't happy.

48. The _____ outfit stuck out in such a staid, somber setting.

49. The man was understandably _____ when given the horrific news.

Word Associations

Select the word or expression that best completes the meaning of the sentence or answers the question, with particular reference to the meaning of the word in **boldface** *type.*

50. An **agnostic** will likely say
   a. "I believe."
   b. "I don't know."
   c. "I'm running late."
   d. "My socks are always missing."

51. Typical **amenities** of urban life might include
   a. air pollution and litter
   b. pedestrians on the street
   c. bridges and cars
   d. museums and concerts

52. Which advice would be most suitable for a person who is **recumbent**?
   a. "Keep your eye on the ball."
   b. "Rise and shine!"
   c. "Turn left at the first light."
   d. "Grin and bear it."

53. A **figment** usually develops in
   a. a factory
   b. an orchard
   c. the human mind
   d. the wild blue yonder

54. If you **temporize** when a decision is called for, you are
   a. acting decisively
   b. stalling for time
   c. misjudging the situation
   d. losing your temper

55. The **motif** of a play refers to its
   a. financial backing
   b. adaptation for television
   c. basic theme
   d. cast of characters

56. The wisest course of action when confronted by a **juggernaut** is to
   a. get out of its way
   b. take its picture
   c. stand your ground
   d. make up your mind

57. **Histrionic** behavior is best suited to
   a. the stage
   b. the laboratory
   c. the classroom
   d. the museum

58. **Primordial** times occurred
   a. in Ancient Greece
   b. first
   c. as a result of negligence
   d. during World War II

59. To **allege** that someone is guilty of a crime means that
   a. the person is clearly guilty
   b. the charge remains to be proved
   c. the charge is malicious
   d. an indictment will be handed down

60. In a **convivial** atmosphere, people may be expected to
   a. suffer from boredom
   b. enjoy themselves
   c. go into shock
   d. show off their erudition

61. You would be well advised not to give **credence** to
   a. your friends
   b. your creditors
   c. a reliable witness
   d. a habitual liar

Choosing the Right Meaning

Read each sentence carefully. Then select the item that best completes the statement below the sentence.

62. The audience's **acclamation** was demonstrated by its repeated standing ovations.

The word **acclamation** most nearly means

a. approval   b. opprobrium   c. asperity   d. victory

63. I was able to guarantee his **collusion** by demonstrating that his participation would be to his benefit.

The word **collusion** most nearly means

a. connivance   b. detritus   c. chicanery   d. foible

64. The knights had retreated into their **bastion**, where they hoped to regroup and repel the invaders' attack.

The word **bastion** most nearly means

a. aperture   b. facade   c. fortress   d. significance

65. I would be extremely **chary** of taking up jogging again until the knee injury is completely healed.

The word **chary** most nearly means

a. benign   b. fecund   c. bestial   d. wary

66. It was fun to watch the two puppies **cavort** in the field, dashing round and round the bushes and trees.

The word **cavort** most nearly means

a. grouse   b. regret   c. gambol   d. rebuff

67. I appreciated the **celerity** with which the electricians responded to the power outage from the storm.

The best definition for the word **celerity** is

a. propriety   b. promptness   c. propinquity   d. verbiage

68. The critic's review turned into a **diatribe** against contemporary music in general.

The word **diatribe** most nearly means

a. badinage   b. surveillance   c. tirade   d. accusation

69. Although the man did not plan the crime, his participation in the robbery attempt was evidence of his **complicity**.

The word **complicity** most nearly means

a. animadversion   b. collusion   c. exigency   d. idiosyncrasy

70. With books and clothes strewn everywhere, the bedroom was in a state of **disarray**.

The word **disarray** is best defined as

a. largesse   b. paroxysm   c. disorganization   d. reconnaissance

WORD LIST

The following is a list of all the words taught in the Units of this book. The number after each entry indicates the page on which the word is defined.

abject, 72
abrogate, 138
abstruse, 166
acclamation, 110
accost, 24
acquisitive, 14
acuity, 62
aesthetic, 148
affront, 166
agnostic, 72
allay, 90
allege, 100
ambient, 138
amenity, 186
animadversion, 24
aperture, 186
arrant, 100
arrogate, 14
askance, 128
asperity, 138
atrophy, 52
attenuate, 128
avid, 24

badinage, 100
banal, 14
bastion, 52
beatific, 176
behemoth, 176
belabor, 14
benign, 128
bestial, 90
blandishment, 176
brackish, 24
bucolic, 110
burnish, 138

cabal, 138
cacophonous, 176
calumniate, 110
canard, 166
captious, 166
carping, 14
cavil, 128
cavort, 34
celerity, 24
charlatan, 128
chary, 110
chicanery, 176

cognizant, 166
coherent, 14
collusion, 110
complicity, 72
conciliate, 100
concord, 52
congeal, 15
consign, 176
consummate, 52
contrite, 166
convivial, 90
coterie, 90
countermand, 100
counterpart, 90
coup, 176
credence, 34
cynosure, 167

decimate, 128
decorous, 167
decry, 34
defunct, 148
deign, 167
delectable, 138
delineate, 62
demur, 90
depraved, 62
deprecate, 139
derelict, 72
desiccated, 167
detritus, 139
devious, 24
diatribe, 72
dilettante, 110
disarray, 52
discomfit, 148
dissemble, 34
dissidence, 186
distraught, 34

ebullient, 139
echelon, 100
eclectic, 139
efficacy, 167
effigy, 72
effrontery, 91
embellish, 91
emulate, 15

encomium, 15
enervate, 62
engender, 167
ephemeral, 91
epicurean, 186
equity, 73
eschew, 15
esoteric, 62
espouse, 148
ethereal, 167
eulogy, 34
euphemism, 177
evince, 34
exacerbate, 101
exhume, 35
exigency, 52

facade, 168
fatuous, 101
febrile, 177
feckless, 35
fecund, 62
felicitous, 91
fetish, 148
fiat, 63
figment, 63
flaccid, 139
flotsam, 53
foible, 129
forgo, 129
fraught, 129
frenetic, 53
furtive, 91

gainsay, 177
gambit, 25
garish, 91
garner, 63
germane, 15
ghoulish, 168
glean, 53
gregarious, 148
grouse, 53

halcyon, 25
hallow, 63
hapless, 149
histrionic, 25

idiosyncrasy, 63
ignominy, 63
illusory, 91
imminent, 177
impeccable, 149
impecunious, 139
imperturbable, 111
importune, 149
improvident, 186
inane, 73
incarcerate, 53
incendiary, 25
incongruous, 168
increment, 111
incumbent, 53
indictment, 73
indigent, 92
indubitable, 73
inexorable, 139
iniquity, 186
innate, 177
inordinate, 92
insatiable, 15
intermittent, 73
interpolate, 149
intransigent, 15
inure, 129
invidious, 16
inviolable, 187
irrefutable, 101
irreparable, 149

jettison, 92
jocular, 53
juggernaut, 101

lackadaisical, 101
laconic, 149
languish, 149
largesse, 16
litany, 101
loath, 177
ludicrous, 54
luminous, 129

macabre, 101
machination, 168
maelstrom, 25

INDEX